Budgeting Skills

A Guide for Nurse Managers

Central Health Studies:

The Central Health Studies (CHS) series is designed to provide nurses and other health-care professionals with up-to-date, informative texts on key professional and management issues and human skills in health care.

The Consulting Editor:

The series was conceived by John Tingle, BA Law Hons, Cert Ed, M Ed, Barrister, Senior Lecturer in Law, Nottingham Law School, Nottingham Polytechnic. John has published widely on the subject of the professional and legal accountability of health-care professionals.

Central Health Studies is a joint venture between **Quay Publishing Ltd.**, Lancaster and **BKT Information Services**, Nottingham

Central Health Studies
Consulting Editor: John Tingle

Budgeting Skills

A Guide for Nurse Managers

Neil Taylor

**Quay Publishing
BKT Information Services**

CHS

Quay Publishing Ltd
7.1.9 Cameron House
White Cross, Lancaster LA1 4XQ

ISBN   1-85642-037-X

British Library Cataloguing in Publication Data

Taylor, Neil
Budgeting Skills: A Guide for Nurse Managers.
– (Central Health Studies Series)
I. Title II. Series
610.73

ISBN 1-85642-037-x

Reprinted 1994

Designed and typeset by **BKT Information Services**, Nottingham, Specialists in Desktop Publishing, Database Development, and Electronic Media Publishing.

Printed and bound in Great Britain by
Butler & Tanner Ltd, Frome and London

CONTENTS

Preface

The history of NHS financial management in the last twenty years has seen the steady devolution of budget management down the hierarchy. The formation of Area and District Health Authorities in 1974 began the process of change, which continued in the early 80s with the formation of 'Units'. The Griffiths enquiry and the introduction of General Management continued the process, allowing local managers to decide their own structures. In the mid 80s Management Budgeting, quickly superseded by Resource Management, encouraged the establishment of 'cost centres' with accountable managers in the financial sense at relatively low levels in the organisation. The emergence of the internal market in the 90s has merely reinforced this trend by attempting to make the money flow with the patient, closing the accountability circle.

The purpose of this book is not to discuss health service finance, but to provide a text that will equip nurse managers to survive and even thrive in this new environment. It does not demand that the reader has any prior knowledge of finance, and it does not seek to convert the reader into an accountant. It does assume that readers have some experience in the health service and have seen their organisation at work to some extent, so that the examples used will make some sense. The book provides some education in the financial field; basic accounting concepts are introduced and explained where they are needed. In addition skills are taught and developed through examples and exercises. The combination of additional knowledge and practical abilities will give the nurse manager confidence in handling the budget and dealing with finance departments.

The typical reader is taken to be a nurse who is a ward sister or equivalent and is responsible for the budget of the ward, or some aspects of it. Naturally the book will be of value to those who will shortly be taking up such a post, or who aspire to it in the near future. The book has been designed to form the text for a course, and will be of value to students of 'Managing Health Studies' or a 'Health Studies BA'. Nurses outside the NHS hospital environment will also find the topics in the book useful. For example, although it doesn't attempt to cover all the aspects of the financial management of a private nursing home, the problems of managing the budget are similar.

It is possible that I may have strayed across the thin dividing line that separates the legitimate use of examples from sexist stereotyping. The identification of a woman as the nurse manager, and a man as the Unit Finance Officer may be too much for the sensitive on this issue. To them I can only apologise and reassure them that no offence is intended. In a slim, direct book like this it is difficult to avoid these problems, and the case study has been included in order to assist the reader to identify with the material presented. The need for a consistent example to carry through the chapters implied that I had to pick one or other, for each of the roles!

Perhaps I ought to apologise to those nurses reading the book who do not work in a large hospital. The book has relevance in many types of organisation, and I hope that nurse managers in smaller hospitals, nursing homes, etc will find the material useful even though most of the examples are based in the types of institution with which I am most familiar.

The aims of this book are :

(1) To introduce and to explain the language and concepts of budgeting.

(2) To provide sufficient knowledge to develop the nurse manager's confidence in dealing with a budgetary situation.

(3) To enable the nurse manager to become competent to prepare and control a budget.

Confidence is important, but competence is equally so. The content of this book is instructional in nature and includes a variety of numerical and discursive exercises; it introduces the enquiring student to more advanced texts for further study. Examples are gathered from across the public sector to provide cross-fertilisation of good practice, to demonstrate the convergence of the issues in the various services, and to develop flexibility in the face of rapidly changing boundaries.

Each chapter is introduced using the device of a case study which reappears throughout the book. The purpose of this is to pose the main themes for the chapter as questions in the mind of our fictional nurse manager, Judith Stott. These themes are then developed in the body of the text and, at the end of each chapter, there are a number of exercises which could be used as the basis for a teaching programme at college, for in-house courses, or as a guide for self study.

The first chapter introduces the concept of a budget, gives a variety of examples of types of budget, and explaines why they are used. By describing an example of an annual budget cycle, the budget is located in its organisational context.

Successful budget management relies on a clear understanding of the costs which make up that budget. Chapter 2, therefore, sets out the range of methods for analysing costs. The concepts are not complex, and they represent the extent of accountancy knowledge that is needed by the nurse manager.

Chapter 3 deals with the practical problem of preparing a budget. It seeks first to set the activity in the political context of a large organisation like a hospital; the second half of the chapter suggests a step-by-step approach to compiling the annual budget for the coming financial year.

The next chapter addresses the other practical problem for the nurse manager: the need to control spending against the budget. Again, this is set in its context, and there is a discussion of the constraints imposed by the organisation. There is a reference back to Chapter 2, as different costs need to be controlled in different ways.

The issue of value for money is now regarded as central to budget management, and Chapter 5 sets out some concepts to help in understanding this subject. The potential conflicts with 'professional standards' are discussed, and the emerging concept of 'quality' is introduced.

The book concludes with a few general remarks on controversial issues which have recurred through the chapters. Budgeting has been regarded in the past as a technical accounting job that can be safely left with finance staff. It is demonstrated that although some aspects of budgeting are obscured by technical jargon, the need to have control of the budget is central to the successful management of any resource unit. The management of the budget by nursing staff is not a passing initiative of Thatcherism, but will be a permanent part of health provision in the future. A reading list for further study and a glossary of the acronyms used in the book follow Chapter 6.

I would like to acknowledge the input of many of my ex-colleagues at Nottingham Polytechnic. I carry full responsibility for the contents, but many of the ideas have developed from our work together on many projects and courses. Particular mention should be made of Bill Murphy, now of Derbyshire College of Higher Education, who shared in my health service research, and Dr Colin Fisher who first encouraged me into teaching on Budgeting in the NHS and through whom much of this book was conceived. Other colleagues whose contributions were equally vital include Ursula Lyon, Alison Henderson and John Tingle.

I am pleased to acknowledge many colleagues from the health service who have contributed to the development of my ideas. Malcolm Munton, now Finance Director at Nottingham City Hospital, provided the location for much of my early work in the NHS and gave many hours of his time over several years. Pat Sykes and Kevin Turner of Pilgrim Hospital, Boston, kindly helped in the preparation of the 'Elsware Hospital' case study exercise, and Peter Kirk of Leeds General Infirmary provided the data for the Budget Cycle (Figure 1.3). Many others attended our courses and freely contributed their experience and knowledge and so, unwittingly, influenced this book.

Finally, I must express my thanks to my wife, Helen, and our children, Christopher, Jonathan and Alison, who have tolerated the writing phase and have anxiously awaited its completion!

Neil Taylor

December 1991

Chapter 1:   Why Use Budgets?

Case Study

Judith Stott is the Ward Sister of a busy surgical ward in Northton District Hospital. She has been in the post for several years and is well respected throughout the hospital for running her ward effectively and sensitively. She had the opportunity of a promotion to a more senior management position within the District two years ago, but decided that she preferred the routine of life in a ward to a desk-bound job.

The General Manager of the hospital, George Bentley, is seeking to modernise the management systems in the hospital and is determined, together with the Unit Finance Manager, Peter Ward, to introduce ward budgeting. Judith will, of course, be affected by this project and has decided to find out as much as possible about budgeting. She is not against change but she wants to make the best of any opportunities that such changes will give her to improve the service to the customers in her ward.

For this reason she wishes to understand what budgeting is about and what part it plays in an organisation.

Introduction

Virtually all organisations of any size use budgets to plan and control their operations, but in the public sector the technique of budgeting has a pre-eminent place in the management process. It dominates the life of the accountant and is a major concern of all senior managers. In this chapter we shall be exploring the nature of budgeting, the reasons for its use and the way in which it imposes an annual cycle upon the organisation.

The Definition of Budgeting

The term Budget is used in a variety of ways. In politics the 'Budget' is a speech by the Chancellor of the Exchequer on 'Budget Day' in the House of Commons. The speech always contains announcements of spending and tax revenues for the coming financial year, and is accompanied by a series of more detailed publications from the Treasury. This focuses attention on the total planned spending of the government and how that spending will be financed by taxation, borrowing, etc. The word 'budget' is often used to denote the overall cash available to an organisation.

However, the Budget also provides a detailed breakdown for both income and expenditure, and in this book we shall use a broader definition that not only includes the finance available, but also the plans for using that finance and the process by which the spending decisions are made.

A **budget** is an agreed **plan** about the future **operations** of an organisation expressed in **quantitative** terms.

1

- a **plan** in that it expresses the intentions of the organisation as agreed through its management processes. It is not necessarily immutable; changed circumstances will demand a revision to the plan, but it is an agreed working position.
- the budget is about **future operations**, the actions of the organisation, not just of the financial constraints placed upon it. The Department of Social Security will **estimate** the number of Social Fund claimants in the coming year, but will **budget** for payments from the fund. The most familiar form of the budget is in financial terms, but it makes sense in many circumstances to plan the operations of the organisation in physical terms first before converting into money.
- The budget is expressed in **quantitative** terms. It is not simply a vague plan ("we shall take on extra staff", "we shall need to cut back on cleaning") but is fully worked out into figures. "Five additional nurses will be recruited in September", "The ward will need to cope with 30 hours cleaning per week instead of 35".

Examples of Budgets

The **annual budget** is used in most public authorities as the summary document which draws together the plans of the organisation in its many aspects, and summarises them for publication to a variety of audiences. In the commercial world the equivalent is the **master budget**, which combines into one statement the **sales** budget, the **production** budget, the **cashflow forecast**, the **capital investment** programme and many others, each of which represents the firm's plans in one aspect of the organisation. In the public sector the concepts are the same, but the terminology is a little different, and the commonest phrases are defined below; some or all of these will be used by health authorities.

Annual Budget—a statement of the planned spending of the organisation and the sources of finance during a specific financial year. It is also referred to as the **Revenue Budget** to distinguish it from the **Capital Programme** (see below). This could be expressed in great detail: many local authorities produce an extensive volume for each service, but equally the annual budget is summarised into a few lines to fit on the leaflet which accompanies the Community Charge bill. By tradition, in the public sector financial years run from April through to the following March.

The relationship of the Annual Budget with the planning process can be represented by Figure 1.1.

Planning will look forward into the future and will identify certain actions taking place at certain points in time. Its focus is upon the actions, and with programming those actions over the relevant time scale. The annual budget will take the plans and identify the financial implications in

Figure 1.1 Role of Budgeting

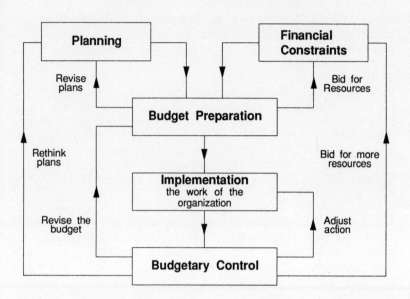

a specific financial year. Attention is addressed to the financial transactions in that period. Budgeting is bound by annual time periods in a manner that need not affect planning.

For example, a ward may be planning the recruitment of an extra member of staff from 1 September 1992. The planning focus is to ensure that job descriptions are written and advertisements placed to attract the appropriate quality of applicant in time, interviews are properly organised, and the best applicant is selected. The budgeting requirement is to include an element in the budget for advertising, and sufficient to pay the new member of staff for 7 months (1 September 1992 to 31 March 1993). For the financial year 1993–94, an additional sum will be needed in the budget to pay the employee for the full 12 months. The **annual budget** will be the main focus for this book.

Manpower Budget—a comprehensive statement of the planned employee numbers, summarised by grade and function. It is also called the **establishment,** and is the basis for the calculation of 'employee costs' in the financial budget.

Capital Programme—a statement of planned investment in land, buildings, plant and equipment. It may also include grants to other bodies for capital investment purposes. Most capital investments will affect the Revenue Budget as they will give rise to increased running costs or savings.

Base Budget—an ambiguous term which is often used in different ways even in the same organisation. It has a specific meaning in relation to Incremental Budgeting (see Chapter 3) as the first stage of preparing an annual budget. It is sometimes used to represent the planned expenditure in **volume** terms, i.e. at a fixed price level. For historical reasons, a specific date in November is often used and budgets are stated at pay and price levels on that date. This facilitates year-on-year comparisons and calculations.

Cash Limit—this represents the budget in ordinary cash terms, and will be calculated as the November price **Base Budget** plus an estimate for the inflation to the end of the relevant financial year. The origin of the term emphasises the unavailability of extra resources beyond the approved budget. If actual inflation proves to be greater than the estimate, the manager must find savings to keep his spending within the cash limit.

Original Estimate—this is the budget as planned and published before the start of the financial year.

Revised Estimate—midway through the financial year, many public service organisations undertake a revision of the budget to take account of changes in circumstances and policies since the original budget was prepared. In some organisations it is called the **Probable** or perhaps the **Near-actual** to reflect the attempt to estimate the likely actual spending for the financial year.

Purposes of Budgeting

In many public sector bodies the Annual Budgeting Process takes up a very significant amount of time and effort. It is necessary to appreciate the reasons behind this investment in order to follow the process itself. There are numerous purposes behind the budget, summarised below into four broad categories. The relative importance will vary according to the type, size and style of organisation but all will be present in some form.

The preparation of the budget provides a process for deciding priorities, and for securing the resources of the organisation. The publication of the budget is a means by which senior management controls activities and reviews the performance of middle management.

(1) **As a process to decide priorities**. In all public service organisations there is insufficient finance to undertake all the possible worthwhile activities. There must be some process by which schemes are accepted or rejected, and the level of resource into each is decided. The Annual Budget process fulfils this role and provides the legitimacy for rejections, namely insufficient resources.

(2) **To secure resources for the organisation**. By law each local authority must publish a budget to accompany the community charge bill to each local resident. Without the budget the bill

would be invalid. On Budget day, the Chancellor uses the planned public expenditure figures to justify changes in taxation. Although District Health Authorities have a cash-limit budget imposed on them, they must produce a Revenue Budget to demonstrate that their planned activities can be afforded within the limit. NHS Hospital Trusts are also required to produce budgets and business plans on a regular basis to the DoH. Some budgets are prepared in order to bid for resources from a funding body. For example, a university will seek funding from one of the research councils by submitting a budget for a research project. Major capital investment funds are often made available to DHAs through a bidding exercise to the Regional Health Authority (RHA).

(3) **To communicate, coordinate and control activities within the organisation**. Agreed budgets are the formal mechanism for communicating plans to middle managers and delegating the responsibility for implementing them. This is a wide topic which is discussed further in later chapters, but it has implications for motivation and control. In the commercial world, sales targets are used to motivate employees to better performance, and, in the same way in the NHS, 'cost improvement' targets are designed to encourage a constant search for improved efficiency. Coordination is important in circumstances when a number of departments are involved in the same project. The capital programme, for example, with its agreed key dates will ensure that planners, architects, builders, development officers, personnel, etc are all working to the same target dates. Finally, of course, budgetary control provides one mechanism by which managers at all levels can satisfy themselves and their superiors that plans are proceeding as intended. This aspect is explored more fully in Chapter 4.

(4) **To review performance**. It has been claimed that conforming to the budget is the primary aim of most public sector managers, since not meeting the budget figure through significant over- or underspending will lead to trouble. This may be a parody of the truth, but budget conformance can lead to waste, not only in the well-researched phenomenon of year-end spend-ups, but also in worthwhile schemes abandoned through lack of financial flexibility. At institutional levels, much has changed through more relaxed attitudes to virement (switching budget provision from one heading to another) and carry-forward rules (see Chapter 4), but the spend against the budget is still a key performance measure for many managers.

The Budget Cycle

One of the essential characteristics of the Annual Budget is its annuality. It subdivides the continuum of time into a series of periods, years (or even months or weeks), which are treated as discrete entities. There is little rationale for this except pragmatism! Traditionally, governments have chosen to levy taxes on an annual basis, and hence the spending of that money has been accounted for yearly. Most commercial organisations will be more flexible in their planning and operational time periods, but the public sector's reliance on tax revenues is constraining.

There is, therefore, a clear 'annual budget cycle' which culminates in the formal approval of the budget each year, shortly before the financial year begins. The cycle runs on as the year progresses and winds down after the end of the year when a comparison is made of actual spending against the budget; but by this stage the next cycle is well under way.

Central government has a well-established system called the 'Public Expenditure Survey' which combines the budgeting procedures of each department and provides a mechanism for ministers to compare and prioritise spending proposals across all the public services. A final document is published annually called the *Public Expenditure White Paper* (PEWP), giving the government's annual spending plans for the coming year. It also usefully includes actual spending for previous years and preliminary estimates for future years for comparative purposes. Work on PEWP turns out to be a continuous job throughout the year for budget officers and Treasury officials as preparations begin at least 18 months in advance of the financial year in question. In smaller organisations the time required is much shorter, but the principles are the same.

Figure 1.2 Planning and budgeting

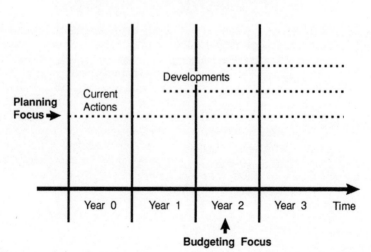

The budget timetable shown in Figure 1.3 has been derived from the processes of a major NHS trust hospital. The shaded area represents the financial year under consideration and the cycle demonstrates the timing of the budgetary activities that occur before, during and after that year.

Fig 1.3   Annual Budget Cycle

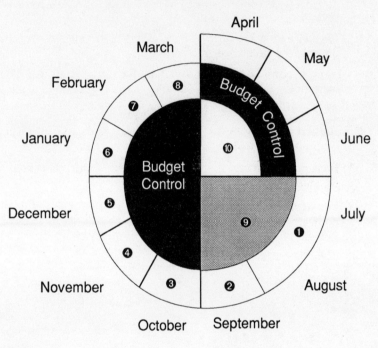

KEY:

1. Review of contracts with DHA and GP fundholders.

2. Estimate likely volume of workload for next year.

3. Negotiations between budget holders and unit accountant.

4. Completion of base budget at November prices.

5. Estimate total contract income. Estimate inflation to the end of next year.

6. Refine workload estimates for next year and complete preparation of the annual budget.

7. Approval of budget by Trust Management board and issue of price lists.

8. Issue approved budgets to budget holders.

9. Revision of workload estimates for the current year.

Exercises

1.1 Discuss the position of Judith Stott in the Case Study at the beginning of this chapter. (see page 1)

   (i) Identify the new tasks and roles that she will need to develop as budget manager for the ward.

   (ii) To what extent are these tasks different from those which she had before?

   (iii) Identify the opportunities that she has in managing the budget to improve the effectiveness of her ward.

1.2 Obtain a copy of the approved budget document for your organisation.

   (i) Identify the main users of this document.

   (ii) Identify reasons for preparing the budget other than communicating to the main users.

   (iii) Enquire about the time and effort expended in the preparation of the budget. Who was involved and why?

   (iv) Compare the budget cycle in your organisation with the model given in this chapter. In what ways is it different? Can you identify reasons why management have chosen their method?

Chapter 2:   Analysing Costs

Case Study

Judith Stott has been receiving budget statements for her ward for a number of months. It divides her costs into pay and non-pay, and is shown below. Previously, it has been unnecessary for her to understand the costs of the ward and she has never taken much notice of the budget statements unless her manager pointed out an overspending. Even then she has always given a satisfactory explanation, and there has never been a problem. She suspects, however, that she will need to understand the finances of the ward much better if she is to manage her budget successfully.

	Annual Budget 1991–1992	Spending up to 31st October
Pay		
Basic Pay	£94,700	£55,120
Overtime	£6000	£4070
Employer's National Insurance	£10,500	£6150
Superannuation	£10,000	£5860
TOTAL PAY	£121,200	£71,200
Sterile Supplies	£8,700	£5010
Non-sterile Supplies		
Furniture & Equipment	£3000	£2870
Miscellaneous	£1600	£490
TOTAL NON-PAY	£13,300	£8370
TOTAL COST	£134,500	£79,570

Introduction

Before exploring budgets any further it is essential to grasp the various ways in which costs are analysed. A manager's power over his budget depends on his knowledge not only of the totality of costs, but also in the suitable subdivision of those costs into appropriate categories. In this chapter we shall explore a range of different methods of analysing costs and the circumstances in which each would be useful to the manager. We shall conclude by mentioning further cost concepts that are useful in the management of a budget.

Accountants' Analysis

The accountancy profession has a highly developed system for analysing expenditure which has been handed down by tradition. We shall start this chapter by identifying the main features of the accountants' system. The primary distinction is between capital and revenue expenditure. In the NHS, as in most of the public sector, these are financed from different sources, and so a separate tally of capital and revenue costs is essential for the accountant.

Revenue costs[†] are those which represent the day-to-day running costs of the organisation, and will normally be planned for in the Annual Budget. Capital costs consist of the acquisition of items (often called capital assets) which are of value to the organisation for a number of years. Land, buildings, plant, equipment and vehicles are the most common sub-headings. In the NHS, capital costs are only deemed to include equipment over a specific value (currently £1000) to save keeping excessive records of small items. DHAs and NHS Trusts are now required to provide for depreciation of capital assets in their revenue costs to reflect the deterioration of each asset over its useful life. The DoH has provided detailed regulations for the calculation of depreciation.

In traditional accounting practice, which was initially designed in a manufacturing context to aid cost control, revenue costs are analysed into Labour, Materials and Overheads. Overheads are further divided into production overheads, those directly concerned in the manufacturing process, and sales and administration overheads which represent costs more remote, but no less important to the success of the firm. This type of analysis may be appropriate in certain sectors of the health industry such as sterile service units but elsewhere an alternative approach is needed.

The NHS has always been strong in the analysis of costs by 'function'. This is the form in which the accounts are presented to Parliament, and so this is the form imposed upon the RHAs and DHAs. An overview of this analysis is shown in Figure 2.1.

In the late 1970s Professor McGee of Cardiff University developed an alternative form of account presentation called 'Specialty Costs', which has gained some credibility and is now required by the DoH from hospitals. The purpose of this analysis is to compare the cost per patient for

† *Beware of the term 'revenue': it is used with several distinct meanings*

Figure 2.1 Accountant's Analysis

Direct Patient Services	Indirect Support Services
Direct Treatment Services	**Expenditures**
Medical/Dental Staff	Administration
Nursing Staff	Medical Records
MSSE	Finance
Pharmacy	Catering
	Domestic/Cleaning
Diagnostic and Other Support Services	Portering
	Laundry and Linen
Radiology	Transport
Pathology	Estate Management
Electrocardiology	Miscellaneous
Medical Physics	
Nuclear Medicine	**Credits**
Audiology	
Physiotherapy	Staff Housing
Speech Therapy	Miscellaneous
Occupational Therapy	
Social Work	
Medical Photography	
Chiropody	

a specialty between health authorities, to aid in the allocation of resources and the identification of good and poor value for money. The principle is based on the allocation of costs according to the category of the patient who benefited. Thus, medical salaries, pharmacy costs, radiology and all the direct costs of patient services are subdivided across the range of specialties that benefit from each. In some cases this is a clear distinction (e.g. consultants), but in others the apportionment is a matter of judgement (e.g. multi-specialty ward costs).

There has been much discussion of 'patient costing', the identification of all costs to the individual patient who benefits. Although this is common in the USA, few hospitals have attempted it in the UK because of the enormous cost of running such a system and the lack of obvious benefits. The alternative which has developed from the resource management initiative is the use of 'cost centres' for accounting purposes. This has been styled 'commander accounting' because it identifies each cost to a manager (or commander) who is responsible for controlling it and bases the accounting systems around the management structures. The use of cost centres and commander accounting is the cornerstone of the delegation of budgets. Cost centres may, of course, follow either a functional pattern or a specialty pattern or indeed any other according to the management structure; in practice, a mixture will be used, complicating the understanding of the finances of the organisation.

Thus, costs centres are now used as the primary basis for accounting analysis, but the further subdivision of costs within the cost centre is also significant. In the NHS, apart from the simple split between pay and non-pay costs, there has not been any standardised approach, and accountants and managers have developed their own systems over a period of time.

Figure 2.2   Accountants' Analysis

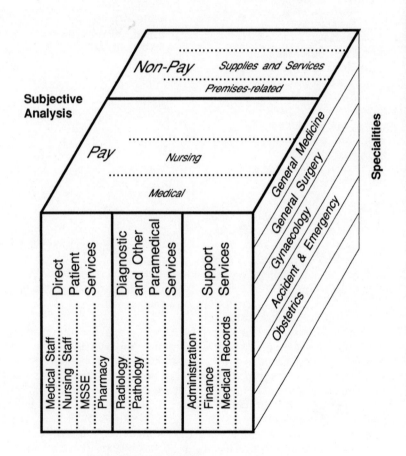

Functional Analysis

In the local authority context, CIPFA has long promoted the concept of a 'standard form' to be used by all authorities to aid comparison. The current version, approved in 1985, is shown in Figure 2.3 and could form a suitable basis for many parts of the public sector, although its adoption in full is certainly inappropriate for the NHS.

Figure 2.3   Standard CIPFA Form

Employees
Salaries and Wages
National Insurance
Superannuation
Other Expenses

Premises-Related Expenses
Repair and Maintenance
of Buildings, Fixed Plant
and Grounds
Energy Costs
Rates
Water Services
Fixtures and Fittings
Cleaning and Domestic
Supplies
Premises Insurance

Transport-Related Expenses
Vehicle Running Costs
Contract Hire
Public Transport
Car Allowances
Transport Insurance

Supplies and Services
Equipment, Furniture
and Materials
Catering Supplies
Printing, Stationery and
Office Supplies
Communications and
Computing Costs
Miscellaneous Expenses

Agency and Contracted Services
Other Authorities
Government Departments
Voluntary Associations
Private Contractors

Transfer Payments
Pupils and Students
Social Services Clients
Housing Benefits

Central, Departmental and Technical Support
Use of Shared Buildings
Central Support Services
Departmental Administration
Democratic Representation

Capital Financing Costs
Loan Repayments
Principal
Interest
Finance Leases

Income
Government Grants
Other Grants and
Contributions
Sales
Fees and Charges
Rents
Interest

Budgeting

Recognition of Events

Many budgeting problems for service managers spring from the timing of the recognition of the 'event' of each cost. Accountants are naturally secure in their knowledge of the ordering and payments procedures, but this issue does cause much confusion for those outside the finance profession. The possibilities are many, and as an example, the various stages for a purchase are shown in Figure 2.4.

Figure 2.4   Recognition of Events

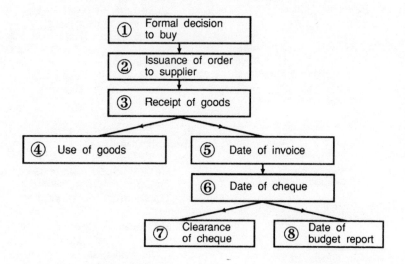

The 'event' is the purchase of an item of pharmacy stock. The issue is: at what point is the purchase recognised in the accounts and under what circumstances should the manager pay attention to the timing of each? The details are described below.

1.   This is a key date for the budget manager. Having decided to spend a portion of his budget on one item, that finance cannot be used for anything else. A well-organised manager may even have earmarked much of his budget for particular items long before the start of the financial year.

2.   This is the point at which a commitment is given; there is now no opportunity to use this finance on any other item, so from a budgeting point of view, it is spent. Ideally, the manager would probably prefer to see this item deducted from the budget at this point to prevent any impression that the budget is still available.

14

3. This is the important date recognised by accountants for the 'correct' entry of the purchase into the accounts. For goods received at the end of one financial year, even though payment is not made until the following year, an 'accrual' or 'creditor' should be set up. Most large organisations will ignore small trivial amounts, but will have formal procedures for identifying significant purchases received but not paid for.

4. As the item is purchased for use later, then if the item is still in store at the end of the financial year, the accountant will want to 'accrue' the cost to the following financial year so that the 'event' will be recognised in the revenue budget for the year in which it is actually used.

5. The date of the invoice is important for VAT purposes and in the absence of an identifiable 'goods received' date, it would be used to decide which financial year must bear the cost.

6. Many public authorities' accounting systems will capture data about the expenditure only at the time that the cheque is produced. This is, therefore, the earliest date that the cost can be shown on a computerised budget-control statement.

7. Small businesses will be concerned about the date of cheque clearance, but the budget manager in a large organisation can leave such worries to the corporate treasurer.

8. Many public bodies are well developed with information technology throughout the organisation, but there are still many budget managers who rely on a monthly print of the state of their budget. In this case, it will be the month-end after the issuance of the cheque before the payment is recorded against the budget. This date may typically be several months after the formal decision to buy.

For many years, pundits have been pressing public bodies to install commitment accounting systems to bypass this delay. Wise budget holders have kept manual records of their expenditure (essentially entered at point 1 or 2) and have relied on these records rather than the official budget statements from Finance. To be fair, there are considerable technical problems in the introduction of commitment accounting systems, and many managers will still prefer to keep their records anyway. Besides, as will be explained in Chapter 4, such a system would only help with a small proportion of budget headings. The manager who chooses to rely on Finance to keep them informed on the current state of their budget must recognise that some of the information will be 8 weeks or more out of date.

Cost Behaviour

Another way of analysing costs, again derived from manufacturing industry, is useful in decision-making and cost estimation. It requires the existence of a reasonable measure of output or service volume (e.g. number of patient bed-days in a ward), and in broad terms seeks to characterise the relationship between each cost and the volume of output.

All organisations will have **fixed costs**, which do not vary over a range of output volumes. For example, the premises costs of a ward, such as heating and lighting will be the same regardless of the number of patients treated, and the pharmacy manager's salary will not vary depending on the volume of drug usage. In many cases, costs of employees will be largely fixed, as they are often based on a fixed 'establishment', the approved staffing level for that unit.

At the other extreme are **variable costs** which are so called because they are directly proportional to the level of output. One would expect the laundry recharge to a ward to be dependant on the number of items sent for washing, which in turn should be proportional to the number of patient-days. The cost of theatre supplies will be related to the number of operations, other things being equal.

Figure 2.5:   Cost Behaviour

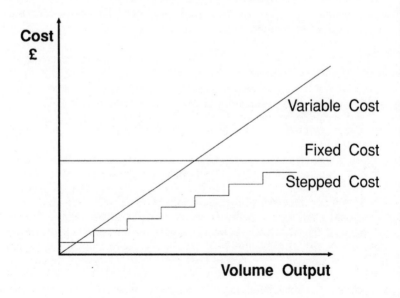

16

If all expenses were either fixed or variable then a model of the costs of the unit would be simple. In practice most costs are semi-variable, that is, they have an element of both fixed and variable cost. One of the most common semi-variable cost is the **stepped cost** (see Figure 2.5) which could apply to staffing in a large ward. As the number of patients increases the staff could cope until a threshold is reached and another nurse is required. Similarly in other disciplines, the volume of caseload will often determine the volume of resource, probably on this stepped basis.

This tool of financial analysis can be very powerful in the estimation of costs, given a predicted volume of demand. We shall be using it in the next chapter as the basis for preparing budgets.

Managers in the NHS will recognise the flaw in this model; that given a growth in demand, senior management will often resist the deployment of further resources and will expect the cost centre to cope, often resulting in an increase in productivity and sometimes in a reduction in quality. The internal market may resolve some of these problems with time, but the ultimate constraint lies with central government financial procedures which are based on fixed cash limits, financed from finite taxation revenues.

Controllability of Costs

This fourth method of analysing costs draws upon the extent to which the budget manager is able to influence the level of the expense on a day-to-day basis. It is a shock to many newly promoted managers that they have very little influence on their budget in the short to medium term, and can only make decisive changes with support from further up the hierarchy.

Figure 2.6 (overleaf) shows the four categories which will be examined further, and demonstrates how they are grouped in to two sections, controllable and non-controllable costs.

It is a particular feature of the public services that many costs are incurred directly in response to a client who cannot be refused, i.e .the cost is **demand-led**. At a national level, unemployment benefit is demand-led (at least in the short-term), since if an individual presents himself and is eligible, then the Department has no alternative but to pay. The accident and emergency service is demand-led, although the technique of the 'queue' is used to attempt to spread demand by keeping some waiting for service. For pure demand-led services, it is clear that the budget manager cannot be held responsible for the volume of service, and hence the cost; however, he may be expected to use his judgement to make a realistic forecast of demand to ensure that sufficient is retained in the budget for these items.

For many years, the drugs budget in the NHS was demand-led. The doctor prescribed, the patient collected, and the NHS paid. For obvious reasons of cost control, the government has introduced various measures to

Figure 2.6   Controllability of Costs

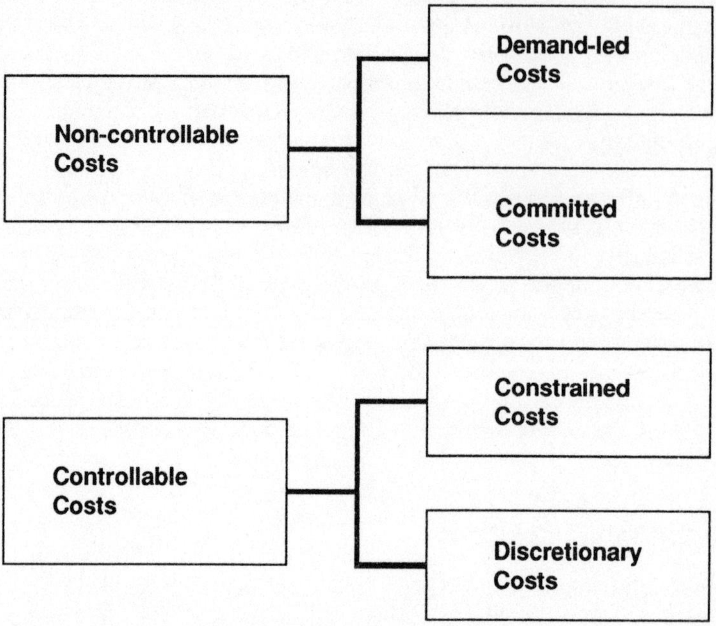

constrain this cost: firstly, prescription charges to discourage trivial usage, then limited drug lists; and more recently, GP indicative budgets. Even within the hospital service, control over the volume of drugs used has been problematical, being based on exhortation and peer pressure amongst consultants. As a consequence, drug costs have taken an increasing proportion of hospital expenditure and have restricted the amount available for other costs within the overall cash-limited budget of the hospital.

In addition to the demand-led costs, there will be a range of other costs over which the budget manager has no control because they are **committed**. Some costs will be committed by law, for example, rates on business premises. Others will be committed by contracts such as interest on loans, maintenance agreements on plant and machinery and, more significantly, salaries and wages to existing staff. Naturally, few of these will be committed in the long term—staff can be made redundant, loans can be repaid, etc.—but for the budget manager handling this or next year's budget, these items represent commitments, unless there is a major policy shift.

Some items are open to influence by the budget manager, but only at the margins, and these are called **constrained costs**. Heating costs, for example are constrained by the requirement to maintain minimum temperatures at places of work, and overtime payments will be driven by the need for adequate staffing cover. However, both of these can be influenced by a manager seeking to economise. Naturally, the distinction between constrained costs and committed costs can be blurred, and will depend upon the policies of the organisation.

Discretionary costs are those with which the manager makes a choice with each purchase. The concept does not imply that the item is any less important, but rather emphasises the manner in which the budget is managed. The usual example is equipment, where a fund is established and purchases are made from it whenever a reasonable case can be made. Discretionary budgets are often held by senior management, cautious about delegating such matters. Typically, the pharmacy may have an equipment heading to include repair and maintenance of existing equipment, replacing worn out machines and, if any is left, purchasing new items. Similarly, the sister in a geriatric ward may have a budget for 'patient comforts', and the decision must be made whether to buy furniture, televisions or Christmas presents for the residents.

These four categories of cost, rather than being distinct, represent a spectrum from the absolutely non-controllable to the purely discretionary. Some costs fall naturally into certain parts of the spectrum; the location of others on the scale depends upon the culture of the organisation and the way in which the costs are managed. For example, demand-led costs are a problem for cost control, but by introducing management review of each case into the process (such as in the Social Fund of the DSS), they become a discretionary cost that can be refused if the budget is tight. Many organisations, when short of funds, will convert overtime into a discretionary cost, requiring senior management approval. Conversely, a ward sister, in giving all nursing staff access to the stock cupboard, is making purchase of stock items into a demand-led cost.

The appropriate analysis of costs into these four categories will assist greatly in the planning and control of your budget, and these categories will be used in later chapters.

Other Types of Cost

Accountants and economists have created a variety of terms to describe all sorts of costs beyond those outlined above. In this book, two further types of cost will be defined as they may be useful to managers in considering their budgets.

Opportunity costs are not real expenses, but represent the benefits that are being foregone by choosing a particular option and by necessity rejecting other options. For example, a bank may wish to rent a portion of the hospital foyer to establish a sub-branch; your senior management, however, may decide that it is more important to use the space as an enquiry/reception desk to assist patients and visitors. The rent that could have been earned from the bank is being given up for the greater benefit of the organisation, and is an opportunity cost of the decision.

An opportunity cost may not be measurable in financial terms. An outpatients manager may feel obliged to dispense with the WRVS teashop to provide more space for an expanding demand. The opportunity cost will be the goodwill of the voluntary workers who are being replaced by a coffee machine!

External costs are those which are passed on to people or bodies outside your organisation by your decisions. In the NHS there are many external costs that must be considered. It has become the habit of many hospital outpatient clinics not to issue prescriptions; instead a note is sent back to the patient's GP advising on the drugs to be prescribed. This undoubtably saves the hospital drug budget but merely transfers the expenditure to the GP's drug budget: the net effect on the NHS finances is zero. In addition there is an external cost to the patient in having to visit the GP surgery before the medicine can be obtained. A hospital may choose to build a new outpatients suite on an area of land previously used for car parking. An external cost imposed upon patients and visitors and perhaps staff will be the inconvenience of parking further from the facilities.

Summary

This chapter shows how costs can be analysed in a number of different ways. It explores traditional accounting analyses and examines the timing of the recognition of purchase transactions. It looks at how costs behave as the workload changes, and the extent of the manager's control over those costs.

The final section looks at two further concepts, opportunity costs and external costs, vital to the budget manager. The concepts introduced in this chapter form the basis for the later chapters in the book.

Exercises

2.1 Examine the budget statement for Judith Stott's ward (see page 9).

   (i) To what extent is the whole cost of the ward included in the statement? Identify any costs which have been excluded, and why.

   (ii) Consider the costs of the ward and attempt to analyse them into the groups identified in this chapter.

2.2 Obtain a copy of the budget for your section. Look at the analysis of the costs into the various headings. Are these headings the most convenient for your purposes, or are they established for the convenience of the accountants?

2.3 To what extent do you have a reasonable measure of workload? Can you establish any of your costs which are variable or stepped costs? Identify those costs which are fixed.

2.4 Analyse your costs according to their controllability. List the costs that are demand-led, committed, constrained and discretionary. This may take some time, and will require a more detailed examination of the way in which you treat each item of expenditure.

Chapter 3:   Preparing The Annual Budget

Case Study

The date is November 1991 and Judith Stott has been called into a meeting of middle managers with the Unit Finance Officer, Peter Ward. Peter has asked each person in the meeting to prepare for their cost centre a draft budget for the coming financial year, based on the budget statements that are currently being circulated. Managers are asked to quantify and justify any changes that they would like to incorporate into the figures, but the constraint is that, overall, no additional finance is available. The draft budgets will then be discussed individually with each manager before the totality is presented to the General Manager for approval.

Judith has understood that the only way that she can attract extra resources is to rob her colleagues, and she does not wish to compete with them. She does have some ideas for redirecting her budget to obtain better value for money, but she is unsure of how to proceed and how to present them to Mr Ward.

Introduction

This chapter will deal with the issues involved in the preparation of the annual budget and the problems inherent in the process. The annual financial budget is the core of every budgeting procedure of all the public-sector bodies. However, many of the issues apply also to the other types of budget mentioned in Chapter 1, such as the manpower budget. The chapter will examine the approaches that can be used and the dilemmas that will face managers with each, but will start by returning to the definition of budgeting from Chapter 1 and looking at the political issues in developing a budget.

Budgets in Large Organisations

A budget was defined in the first chapter as an agreed plan about the future operations of an organisation expressed in quantitative terms. The budget, as a statement of the agreed plan for the organisation, must be agreed at the relevant level of authority; in the case of a District Managed Unit, this will be the District Health Authority. For an NHS Trust, the Directors will have primary responsibility, although the RHA and the DoH will also have an interest.

Budgeting must be closely related to planning, and the budgets must develop from, and be a quantitative statement of, the plans of an organisation. A budget which has no ground in planned actions is merely a statement of resources available; to become an effective budget it must be derived from the intentions of the managers in employing people, in purchasing goods and services, etc. Thus in considering the development of a budget, attention must be directed towards the planning processes. Indeed, in many organisations the preparation of the budget is the mechanism for planning, although at a strategic level this should not be true in the NHS; the DoH and RHAs have extensive planning systems for DHAs and hospitals.

Rational Budgeting

In an ideal world, the budget would be based upon a rational evaluation of 'need'. In the NHS this would involve the assessment of each type of treatment and the good that it does to the 'health' of the population, with priority being given to the most effective procedures. The budgets for the various departments would be based upon a rational calculation of the finances required to deliver the agreed level of service, and there would be care to ensure that resources were allocated fairly between geographical areas.

Figure 3.1   Rational Budget Model

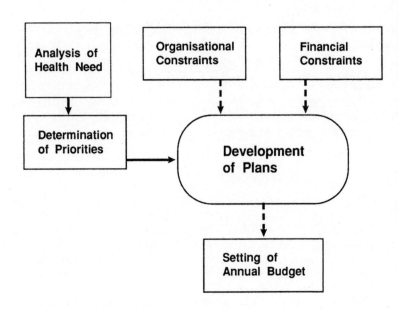

Unfortunately, this ideal is unattainable, although elements of it can be used as a target to aim for. The reasons for this, which are related to one another, are discussed below:

(1) There is no agreed definition of 'need' in the health service, nor in any other public service either. Indeed, there is no common understanding of the meaning of the word 'health' that is sufficiently robust to be a basis for making detailed resource allocation decisions. Thus the concept of 'rationality' in evaluating health needs is difficult to apply, and inevitably descends to personal and political priorities.

(2) Secondly, even if there were some consensus on the above points, there is a major problem in the availability of information. In any large organisation, and especially in hospitals, expertise is spread widely across the departments, and strategic management is dependent upon the advice of specialists in evaluating services. There are inevitably plenty of options presented for growth, but few for cuts! Of course, senior managers faced with the need to make cuts will make the best possible decisions, but the ideal presented above will be far from achieved.

(3) The third point relates to the political nature of public services and the need for decisions to be 'acceptable'. It may be the correct rational action to close down a children's ward, but where there is a high level of public pressure, it would be a bold general manager who proceeded with it. In the health service, there are many groups who have a stake in the organisation and will demand a say in its actions. This includes internal groups like the senior management team, the consultants and the health unions. Also there are external groups with official rights: the DHA, RHA, FHSA, the Community Health Council, and those with political power such as the MP and the press (as representing public opinion). It is no surprise that many general managers see their role primarily as political, maintaining a coalition of interests, rather than the rational manager applying analytical techniques to determine the best solution to each problem.

The Processes of Budgeting

There are two processes in budget preparation which will both occur at the same time. They are of equal importance, yet will usually lead to conflict and negotiation, and it is the interface between these two processes which leads to the final agreed budget.

Top-down budgeting is the process of allocating the available resources between the various functions/activities/departments of the organisation. It is undertaken at a strategic level and, in theory, takes

Figure 3.2   Top-down & Bottom-up Budgeting

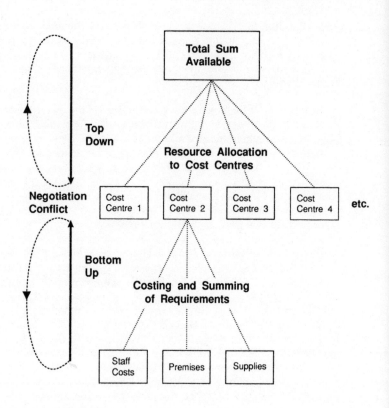

account of available information, priorities, demands etc. to determine a fair distribution of the finance.

Bottom-up budgeting begins at the operational level of the organisation, and consists of the calculation of the finance required to enable the manager to deliver the service expected. This process is sometimes called 'costing' and depends on an operational plan which will identify the numbers and grades of staff required, the materials and equipment, the premises and other resources which contribute to the service. Against each of these are inserted the appropriate financial figures, and the total is obtained.

The negotiation process begins when the total finance available turns out to be less than that required to deliver the services. Savings must be found, either to deliver the service more cheaply (increase efficiency and/or productivity) or to cut the quantity or quality of the service. The activities tend to be circular, with both top-down and bottom-up processes being repeated until there is agreement in the middle. The precise methods used will be unique to any one organisation, but research has indicated a series of models which are often adopted by strategic management tends to use to reaching an agreement on budgets. Relatively few use a dictatorial approach which imposes budgets without discussion.

The nurse manager, with a cost centre to run, is involved at different levels with both processes; the bottom-up to negotiate the overall level of resources for the cost centre, and the top-down to allocate those resources between the services provided.

Allocating Resources

The interface between these two processes can be characterised in the following systems for resource allocation:

(1) **Formula Funding** is widely used in the public sector as a means of allocating resources in a fair and acceptable manner. The formula is determined in advance by the strategic management based on a series of indicators of need combined into some mathematical expression which will give the resources for each unit. The RAWP formula was used for many years to distribute total NHS finance between the Regions, and by some Regions to distribute to District Authorities.

Under this system, the resources for each unit will be non-negotiable initially, but inevitably there will be some managers who will exert informal pressure to get the weightings in the formula adjusted. The system has the appearance of equity and impartiality, but the selection of the factors and their weighting in the formula leaves as much scope for political manipulation as any other system.

At the bottom end, however, operational management must adjust their plans to reflect the resources available. Decisions are dominated by the Top-Down element.

(2) **A Zero-Base Bidding** system can be used at the interface between the bottom-up and the top-down processes. Each unit is asked to prepare its requests for funds, which will be considered and evaluated by senior management. Although a zero-base may be the intention, in practice most activities cannot be reduced to zero either in the short or medium term because they are legally or politically committed. The manager, therefore, will be asked to

prepare his plans based on a series of resource assumptions above and below existing levels. Senior management will then evaluate each of these packages and allocate the resources accordingly.

This is close to a 'rational' system, in that senior management is given the information to select the optimum resource allocation package from the offered bids from the middle management. However, it does require management at all levels to be impartial in the provision and evaluation of information. It assumes that there are some agreed criteria for deciding priorities and that managers have the time and energy to invest in a time-consuming process that may not work to their advantage. Zero-base budgeting models were introduced into certain American Federal Agencies in the 1960s but were soon abandoned as too demanding and insufficiently responsive to political necessities.

(3) **A Simple Bidding** system is sometimes used by organisations as a less onerous alternative. Each section manager is asked to make a bid for resources, and these bids are challenged only if they are excessively different from expectations (usually based on last year's spending). All the accepted bids are then be summed, which almost certainly lead to an excess over resources available. These excesses are eliminated by a percentage cut off each budget, or some similar device.

This system is practical and has the advantage of appearing to treat all budget holders in the same way: the pain of cuts is spread evenly without requiring any of the difficult decisions (which services to cut) to be made by the strategic management. Such cuts could even be styled as 'efficiency savings' without any evidence that efficiencies are available, or that they should be spread evenly across all budgets. Departments whose costs are all committed will face very different problems from those with substantial discretionary funds.

(4) **Incremental Budgeting** is the simplest of all systems, and hence the most widely used. In this case, the budgets for last year are rolled forward to the new year with adjustments made for known changes. Managers are normally asked for a list of such variations which may arise from demographic changes or technological or legislative requirements.

This system can be operated easily, but it does have a tendency to institutionalise existing spending patterns. Existing budgets are not challenged effectively, leading to the potential for redundant expenditure—costs incurred which no longer serve any purpose for the organisation. However, a vigilant manager will always be looking for such possibilities within his budget and will have plenty of other uses for those resources!

Preparing the Budget

Regardless of the resource allocation systems used by senior managers, which may change from year to year, there will be an obligation upon the nurse manager to prepare a budget, a working document to input into that process. It will represent the planned action, and will form the basis for the top-down/bottom-up negotiations. As indicated above, the simplest approach is to use last year's budget and adjust it for known changes.

The incremental approach has a number of advantages. Firstly, by basing next year's plans on the events of this year, the manager is less likely to make serious mistakes, for example, forgetting to include a whole area of spending. Secondly, large organisations move slowly, so it would often be unwise to propose radical change within a short timescale. Thirdly, much of the activity in public services is committed by legislation or by politics. Finally, most aspects of the infrastructure, buildings, equipment and staff are difficult to change.

There is a need, however, to counter the problem of redundant expenditure by re-examining the budget in some way. This section proposes an achievable method for preparing an annual budget, which requires the manager to do some creative thinking, but does not overburden her with a heavy administrative process. A more rigorous approach would expect the manager to rethink his objectives, and this will be discussed in more detail in another book in this series *Business Planning for Healthcare Professionals*, which is strongly recommended for those managers required to produce a business plan. A budget is, of course a far less rigorous document than a business plan, but elements of the processes of producing a plan should be used in the development of a budget..

The manager, in preparing the budget, should work through the stages shown in Figure 3.3 below, and consider the following issues:

(1) The output required, which will be an estimate of the workload of the section through the year.

(2) The processes that will be used to achieve that output, the methods of working, the operational activities that must be supported.

(3) The resources required to maintain those activities (staffing, materials, premises, etc.).

(4) The cost of those resources in the financial year.

Figure 3.3   Preparing the budget

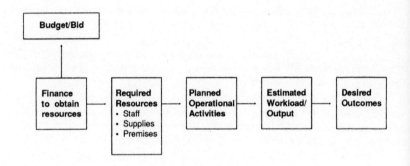

Workload Estimates

Workload could be as simple as the number of patient-days in a ward, or the number of outpatient appointments. Recently a number of more sophisticated systems have been developed which take account of the dependency of the patient, and hence give a fuller picture of workload, but these are by no means universally available. For the nurse manager the primary need is to use a measure that will be robust and convincing in any discussions with senior managers.

An estimate of the workload for the coming financial year will always involve an element of guesswork, but some techniques are available which could improve credibility. Recent history will normally be a good starting point unless there have been changes to the service. There are a number of ways of identifying trends and there are statistical packages available whichcan produce forecasts.

Caution must be applied in the use of statistics; some of the figures produced in the NHS have been regarded as unreliable. Increased diagnosis of a particular complaint, for example, may reflect improved recognition rather than a genuine spread. Firstly, how certain are you of your workload estimates? Is there a clear trend? What level of uncertainty exists? Secondly, if you are using a trend, do you have any explanation that could support it? If you have observed a trend but cannot offer any reason for it, then it may be a statistical accident!

Reviewing Activities

In the light of your estimated workload you may feel that some of your present activities could be improved. The process for doing this will be discussed in the *Business Planning* book. For most managers in most years, however, planning is not so exciting, and last year's activities can be projected forward without too many adjustments. Radical changes in the organisation are usually triggered by some major external factor, such as new legislation, technological advances or market changes.

Reviewing Resources

Having decided the activities that need to occur next year, you can now identify the resource required for them. At this point, you need to establish which of your costs are committed, since in the absence of a major upheaval, you will need to plan around these. There may be a point at which such an upheaval is essential, but not every year. For example, if your ward occupies certain rooms within the hospital building, then it is probable that those resources are unchangeable, and there would be only a marginal effect, even if an extensive reorganisation of the hospital were to be undertaken. Similarly, the level of existing staffing needs to be taken into account. The manager must not feel a prisoner of past recruitment decisions, but likewise cannot hire and fire at will without creating difficulties with staff morale and raising other problems such as industrial tribunal hearings.

It will be useful also to have an understanding of which costs are fixed and which are variable. If an increased workload is expected then resources will not need to be increased in proportion, because within certain limits those costs which are fixed will not change. At this point, care must be taken with the use of regional averages or 'norms', because they may reflect very different operational conditions which may be more or less efficient than yours.

Figure 3.4 shows an example of a budget for nursing hours. Initially, the budget is set at the current workload, but due to a change in the operational procedure the expected total dependency will rise by 5%. On the two day shifts staff are busy continuously so the only fixed costs relate to the management and administration time, about 10% of the total (say). On the night shift, however, on this ward the two staff on duty are not so busy and are primarily there for emergency cover; these hours are therefore treated as a fixed cost which will not need to increase. The fixed costs will not change as a result of the change, but the variable cost should be increased by 5%, in proportion to the increase in workload, so a 5% increase in workload implies a 5% increase in variable hours, but only a 3.9% increase in total hours from 820 to 852.

Figure 3.4 Example of application of Fixed/ variable costs

	Weekly Hours Worked in the Ward				
		Current (analyzed into ...)		Proposed (with 5% increase)	
	Total Hours	Fixed	Variable	Revised Variable	Revised Total
Morning Shift	350	35	315	331	366
Afternoon Shift	350	35	315	331	366
Night Shift	120	120	0	0	120
	820	190	630	662	852

Estimating Costs

Having decided on the resources needed to undertake your activities, to produce the budget it is necessary to apply 'prices' to them to obtain the financial budget. In some cases the prices will be readily available from elements such as pay scales, utility tariffs and other price lists. In other cases you will need to obtain quotations; an inadequate budget at this stage may mean that you will ultimately be unable to obtain the required item.

The budget should as often as possible be derived on the basis of:

Resource Volume × Price

If the resource volume is not known then it is probable that the budget will not actually be a plan, but will merely be a statement of cash available. The manager in submitting his budget should be able to justify each item with the plans indicating how that amount is to be spent. There are few circumstances in which this does become a problem, and they normally relate to discretionary costs. For example, where the manager is responding to claims or bids from third parties which cannot be predicted in advance, then it is only possible to work from past experience. Where however the budget relates to the maintenance and replacement of equipment then the budget needs to be adequate over the longer term to cover the depreciation of the equipment. For example, if a department has 5 similar machines, and their useful life is only 5 years then the budget needs to be sufficient to replace one each year on average.

Finally, once the budget has been built up from the various elements as above, it is important to verify your results in any way that is possible. Comparisons with the previous year may be useful to ensure that no important item has been forgotten. Many managers find it useful to discuss the budget with their deputy and other staff. It would be wise to to meet with the finance staff, if possible, since they are experienced with budgets and may have valuable advice to share.

Treatment of Inflation

Inflation remains a major problem in budgeting (regardless of what it may mean to the economy!). Plans need to be made at a time when there is much uncertainty about the price that must be paid. When the PEWP (see Chapter 1) was first established in the 1960s, the Government used to produce all its budgets at a fixed price level, which was the 1 November previous to the start of the relevant financial year. Any inflation that occurred after that date would be added to the budget headings automatically, and thus the 'volume' of planned expenditure was preserved. This procedure was carried into many parts of the public sector and is still used, at least in part, by many local and health authorities. Nurse managers will recognise one manifestation of this phenomenon as the 'full funding of pay awards'.

In the late 1970s, however, it became clear that this system had some severe disadvantages. First, there was no incentive for managers to keep inflationary pressures down, and this was especially acute in the negotiation of pay rises. Second, because the budgets were at November prices and the actual spending was at real prices, there was often a divergence between the two which looked as if costs were not being controlled effectively; the November price became known as 'funny money'. Thirdly, there was the imperative to restrain the total of public expenditure in cash terms, and hence the necessity for planning in cash terms. So the concept of the 'cash limit' was invented, as the budget which would not be increased even if inflation exceeded expectation.

Apart from pay awards, it is now almost universal practice for budgets to be presented and managed in cash terms, and for many organisations, this is also true of pay budgets. Health Authorities and hospitals are now funded in cash terms, although many retain the problem of funding pay-rises at the strategic level rather than passing it down to budget holders.

For the budget manager seeking to understand the effects of inflation on the budget, the concept of the November Base Budget is a useful one. It eases the calculations in updating the budget from one year to the next, and in the case of the application of a cash limit it provides a basis for evaluating the level of constraint required. Figure 3.5 below gives an example of the use of a November Base budget.

Figure 3.5   Use of November Price

Assumptions:

(1) The original budget at November 1991 base was £100,000.

(2) The pay rises take effect from 1 September each year:

	Estimated	Actual
1992	3%	5%
1993	4%	5%
1994	2%	4%

(3) The actual pay rises have not been fully funded by the authority in the current year, but have in the following year (not always true).

(4) For simplicity, no account has been taken of increments.

	November Base Budget	Funded Cash Limit	Actual Cost	Level of Underfunding
1992–3	£100,000 (Nov 91)	£101,750[3] +3% 7 months	£102,917[4] +5% 7 months	£1167 2% 7 months
	↓+5%[1]			
1993–4	£105,000 (Nov 92)	£107,450 +4% 7 months	£108,063 +5% 7 months	£612 1% 7 months
	↓+5%[2]			
1994–5	£110,250 (Nov 93)	£111,536 +2% 7 months	£112,823 +4% 7 months	£1286 2% 7 months

[1] Actual increase in 1992
[2] Actual increase in 1993
[3] November Base Budget [NBB] + (3% of NBB × $7/12$)
[4] NBB + (5% of NBB × $7/12$)

Summary

This chapter considers the process of preparing a budget. The first part of the chapter discusses the 'political' nature of budget preparation and identifies that, although 'rationality' may be the ideal it is rarely the primary input into budgetary decisions. The second part provides a series of hints into the process of putting together a budget. The emphasis is upon the identification of workload and the grounding of budget figures upon proven needs. The role of the incremental process is also discussed, as is the problem of dealing with inflation.

The exercises at the end of this chapter provide an opportunity to practice the skill of budget preparation. The technical processes may be daunting at first but, as with most things, become easier with practice.

Exercises

3.1 Identify the tasks that Judith must follow in the preparation of her budget.

(i) What type of resource allocation system is being imposed upon her? How would it affect her actions if other systems were used?

(ii) To what extent should she play the 'budgeting game' and use her political influence to attract extra resources for her ward? What risks does she face if she ignores the political aspects?

3.2 Examine the budgeting processes within your organisation.
Classify the systems used into one or more of the above categories. Discuss the extent to which they could be improved.

3.3 **Geriatric Unit**

You are the ward manager of a large geriatric unit located in a separate building in the grounds of a major hospital. It has 35 beds, and because of constant demand is always full. The hospital authorities have decided to proceed with a Resource Management project under which your job has been redefined (you used to be called a nursing officer), and management responsibilities have been delegated to each facility in the hospital.

The date is 15 January 1992 and you have been asked to prepare a draft budget for the financial year 1 April 1992 to 31 March 1993, which will then be scrutinised by the finance officer. You have never prepared a budget before, but you have been provided with the expenditure figures for your unit for the last 3 years, although you do not have complete confidence in their accuracy. In addition, you have found some information of your own which could help. These data are given in the table below:

(a) Prepare a draft budget for submission to the Finance Office using the information available. Your budget should include allowances for pay rises and inflation up to 31 March 1993. Make reasonable assumptions where information is not available.

(b) The Finance Officer has indicated he wishes to discuss your draft budget with you in early February. However, you are going on holiday for a fortnight on January 31 and your deputy will need to stand in for you. Prepare a short note for your deputy that will explain the purposes of the meeting in the context of the whole budgeting process.

WARD EXPENDITURE			
	1989/90 Actual (£)	1990/91 Actual (£)	1991/92 Actual (£)
Nursing Staff	261,890	293,330	324,000
Other Staff	14,950	21,410	46,500
Premises Costs	22,740	28,060	32,000
Cleaning Contract	50,330	52,920	57,000
Medical Supplies	16,720	11,490	13,500
Drugs	5440	8710	10,500
Laundry	16,880	19,350	20,000
Catering	59,370	65,620	70,000
Other Costs	2410	3860	5000
	450,730	503,750	578,500
CURRENT STAFFING	Grade	Annual Pay (£)	Number (FTE)
Nursing Staff	G	18,600	1
	D	13,900	3
	B	10,500	10
	A	9400	12
Other Staff		12,600	1
		8200	1
		6400	3

Notes: It is normal practice to add 18% to the estimated pay budget for employer's National Insurance and pension contributions.

All staff will receive an annual pay rise on 1 April—the amount is unknown but is likely to be 8–10%.

Unit Costs: **Average cost per in-patient day for 1990/91 across the region**

	£
Other Staff	3.6
Premises Costs	2.89
Cleaning Contract	4.21
Medical Supplies	1.12
Drugs	1.35
Laundry	1.6
Catering	4.97
Other costs	0.42

3.4 Mental Health – Community Treatment Service

The Mental Health Unit in a large district health authority has established a division called 'Mental Health – Community Treatment Service' which is responsible for a series of treatments offered in three day centres around the City. A Clinical Director has recently been appointed to the Division, and he wishes to reorganise the budget which has formerly been held at high level in the organisation. He has established four cost centres, one for each day centre and one for the direct medical treatment costs. It is intended that each day centre manager will be responsible for all the aspects of management of the centre, including the building.

Available Information

The financial costs for the past three years of each centre has been identified by the Unit Accountant. The staffing structure of the day centres has not changed. The current financial year has started without any major changes, but the Clinical Director wishes to review this and has asked each centre manager to prepare a budget for the current year.

The unit classifies its clients into three groups for day centre treatment purposes. Category A is the most severe, requiring about double the nursing input of Category C patients.

Required

The date is 1st April 1991. The costs for one day centre are shown below. Take the role of the Day Centre Manager and prepare a draft budget to present to the Clinical Director for the current financial year. He will judge these budget proposals on their merits and will approve a final budget for the Division within the resources that are available.

Budgeting

Additional Information

(a) The pay award for 1 Apr 1991 has been agreed at 6%.

(b) General underlying inflation in Health Service non-pay costs is currently around 8%.

(c) Additional funding for the Unit is 6% higher than last year, but some increase is already committed in service developments in other divisions of the Unit.

(d) The Clinical Director has already indicated that he may be looking to rationalise the service, possibly by closing one of the centres and concentrating on two centres only. He may be looking for the centre with the largest unit cost as a target for closure.

Day Centre Costs			
Annual Accounts for the Year Ended	31 March 1989	31 March 1990	31 March 1991
Expenditure:			
Wages	£92,204	£99,580	£108,542
National Insurance	£7376	£7966	£8683
Superrannuation	£4610	£4979	£5427
Food	£5720	£5980	£6370
Building maintenance	£138	£523	£449
Heating and lighting	£3877	£4148	£4683
Rates	£526	£569	£633
Cleaning materials	£1208	£1275	£1304
Equipment	£3265	£1074	£2152
Staff Advertising	£150	0	£60
Telephone	£549	£487	£531
Other Expenses	£1244	£1387	£966
TOTAL	£120,867	£127,968	£139,800

Statistics Number of Clients	Year Ending 31 March 1989	Year Ending 31 March 1990	Year Ending 31 March 1991
Category A	5	7	10
Category B	25	24	25
Category C	14	15	14
Staffing	Weekly Pay	Full-time Equivalent Staff
Day Centre Manager	£200	1.00
Nurse	£160	6.00
Nursing Assistant	£100	7.00
Cook	£150	1.00
Cleaner	£90	1.00

3.5 Midshire Drug Budget Case Study

Introduction

General practitioners (GPs) are independent medical contractors who diagnose and treat patients on their lists with all sorts of conditions and, if appropriate, refer them on to other health services, mainly hospital in- and out-patient facilities. Until 1991, medicines prescribed by GPs could be obtained from the pharmacist, subject to the payment of a fixed charge for non-exempt patients, and the cost would be met by the Government through the local Family Health Services Authority (FHSA). From April 1991, some GP practices have been allowed to become 'Fund Holders', responsible for a budget for a much wider range of treatments, but this case study concerns those practices which are not fund holders. For them, the cost of all prescriptions issued by the Practice will be accumulated for the financial year by the FHSA and compared with an 'indicative budget'. Those practices that overspend consistently will be subject to scrutiny and investigation by the FHSA.

The Case

You are the General Manager of Midshire FHSA, which covers a small area in the East Midlands. You have the task of determining the indicative drug budget for the GP practices in your area. You have been given the total available from the Department of Health, but have received no advice on the allocation between practices. There are 5 non-fund holder GP practices in Midshire, and you have collected some current and historical data to help you with your task (see below).

Prepare a report for circulation to all interested parties (including the GPs) which recommends and justifies a fair and acceptable method of allocating the prescriptions budget for the financial year April 1991–March 1992 among the 5 GP practices.

Additional Information

(1) Practice 2 covers a large rural area in the eastern half of Midshire.

(2) Practice 3 is in the rough inner-city-like centre of Midtown in the centre of Midshire.

(3) Practice 4 covers a large suburban area in the south of Midtown.

(4) Practice 5 is the only practice in the growing town of Sowmere, 15 miles west of Midtown, and has recently expanded its size to cope with the extra demand.

PRACTICE	1	2	3	4	5
No. of GPs	6	2	5	12	8
No. of Patients on list	7246	2261	6483	15,030	9422
Under 21s on list	2289	481	2451	802	3036
Over 65s on list	870	327	802	1462	1132
Spending History					
1988/90	£95,200	£26,200	£104,400	£169,800	£124,700
1989/90	£108,000	£30,800	£120,100	£197,400	£155,300
Apr–Dec 1990	£89,500	£24,500	£105,200	£160,800	£133,400

Chapter 4:   Monitoring Spending

Case Study

The date is June 1992. Judith's budget was agreed by the Finance Office and she is now working to that budget in the financial year 1992-93. She has received the following budget statement for the first two months of the year showing an overspend in supplies and an underspend in staffing, although she thought that the year was working out as planned. In previous years she would have ignored the report and claimed ignorance, but she now wishes to take responsibility for the actions of her ward and needs to understand what options she has available.

Figure 4.1   Budget Statement Month 2 1992-93

Surgical Ward: 15

Budget Holder: Judith Stott

	Annual Budget	Budget Profile	Actual Spending	Over/ Under
Staffing	£130,000	£20,294	£20,004	£290–
Sterile Supplies	£9,300	£1,550	£1,685	£135+
Non-sterile	£4,600	£767	£1,442	£675+
Total	£143,900	£22,611	£23,131	£520+

Introduction

One of the purposes of budgeting identified in Chapter 1 was to communicate, coordinate and control. Indeed, some managers may only have seen the budget as a means of constraint on the delivery of their service, and control can be the dominant element of budgeting. The exercise about GP budgets in Chapter 3 illustrates that where an organisation chooses to use budgets it is always to control spending and always to adapt the behaviour of the budget holder towards that which would be more beneficial for the organisation.

Senior management in any organisation will be monitoring budgets and calling managers to account if their spending appears to be out of line. It is, therefore, essential that all managers monitor their own expenditure, and take appropriate action before they are required to defend themselves.

Budgeting

This element of self-control demonstrates a commitment to the organisation as a whole and contributes towards its success.

This chapter is concerned with budgetary control, and will discuss the need for appropriate management information to enable you to do the job. Also it explains the range of actions that are available to the manager, if his information suggests to him that the plan is not proceeding properly. But, first you are introduced to the range of controls that will probably be in place in your organisation to prevent overspendings and keep you to the budget.

Physical Controls

In considering the topic of budgetary control many writers ignore the range of physical controls, yet these are probably the most important for many public-sector managers in large organisations. For treasurers and for politicians it is too late when the managers have overspent the budget; there needs to be a series of constraints that make it difficult for this to happen.

The most obvious example is the 'establishment', or manpower budget which among other things performs the task of preventing the manager from employing too many staff, or at higher grades than the budget can support. The establishment is normally the basis for calculating

Figure 4.2 Manpower & Financial Budgets

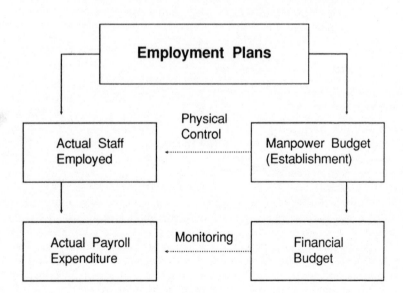

the pay element of the annual budget, so that keeping to the staff numbers will deliver a cost close to the financial provision.

The establishment is available to personnel departments and to the salaries and wages sections of treasurers' departments. It is also often reported on the monthly budget control prints, so the physical number of staff compared with the establishment is public knowledge. Many organisations have official appointment procedures which have the dual purpose of ensuring the proper compliance with employment law and preventing appointments above the establishment, as well as the provision of advice by the personnel officer.

The establishment is a useful tool for senior management, but it does not solve all the problems for the budget holder. It is common for the financial provision to be rather less than the cost of the full establishment, the difference being a 'vacancy' rate. It is assumed that when a member of staff leaves it takes some time to appoint a replacement, so there will be a financial saving during the period of the vacancy. This vacancy provision may be 2%–5% or even more in some cases, and the manager needs to plan how this can be achieved within his budget.

A second major problem which occurs in the NHS is the funding of the establishment at 'midpoint'. The financial provision assumes that your staff are equally distributed across the incremental scale. Those managers with an experienced staff with a low turnover will find that their pay bill will be increasingly greater than the budget as the staff move up the scale, and they will need a plan to be able to make the requisite savings.

In the NHS, staffing represents a high proportion of the total costs, so the establishment has been the most important physical control on spending. However, some authorities also use other systems for the non-pay costs. Central supplies departments probably owe their existence to the possibility of obtaining substantial savings through purchasing in bulk. But they can also be used to monitor the orders issued by each section. Some systems will even reject orders that exceed the budget provision. In addition, although the requirement to use central supplies is usually justified on value for money terms, it also enables senior management to keep a closer check on the volume of purchases. It also saves substantially on the cost of checking and verifying invoices.

Budget Reporting

Even given the level of physical controls, the budget manager still needs to be kept informed of current progress on spending if the budget is to be controlled effectively. Accounting textbooks list the important characteristics of a good budgetary control reporting system as *accuracy, relevance, timeliness and ease of understanding*. In most large organisations there is a computerised financial information service which produces monthly spending reports compared with budget and highlights significantly over– or underspent headings (see Figure 4.1 for a typical example). Some make use of on-line technology and provide the manager with a computer terminal to interrogate the financial system and obtain reports when desired. Others provide only exception reports which list headings that potentially need action, but not those which are in line with the budget.

These reports constitute the 'official' accounts and hence need to be used by all managers. In certain circumstances they need to be supplemented by other sources, but they are especially useful for the following types of budget:

(1) **Budgets where the actual costs require complicated calculation, or are determined by another computer system.** This applies especially to payroll costs, where the payroll system may enter the cost to the accounts even before the employees are paid. The complications arise from the nature of employment contracts as well as statutory requirements like income tax, national insurance and sick pay. Other examples will include recharges from central supplies departments and possibly 'contract' payments by DHAs to hospitals.

(2) **Budgets which consist of a large number of small payments such as day to day food purchases.** In this case the computer is a more effective adding machine, especially for a budget which is not a significant proportion of the total.

(3) **Budgets which are committed or heavily constrained, such as salary and energy costs, particularly across a number of buildings.** The computer enables the manager to monitor progress against the budget where there is little action that can be taken in the short term.

(4) **Budgets which have an irregular profile** (see below). Where the profile is uneven across the months, a computer can calculate the expected spending and give a realistic comparison with actual.

Profiles

Profiles have been used much more extensively over recent years to aid budgetary control. They are constructed from the expected incidence of expenditure against a particular budget heading through the year. Examples are given in Figure 4.3; the expenditure on salaries will be even through the year, month by month, with a probable increase in the month when a pay rise is implemented. Energy costs will have a seasonal pattern, with higher costs in the winter than the summer.

The power of the profile is the ability to predict expected expenditure at any stage through the year. This eases comparisons with actual costs, and can give early warning of budgets that may be overspent at the end of the year. The weakness of profiling is the difficulty in predicting the pattern for certain kinds of cost. An incorrect profile could reassure the manager that all is fine, when it is not. If your organisation uses profiles in its budgetary reports ensure that you understand them and accept the assumptions that are implied in the figures.

Figure 4.3   Typical Profiles

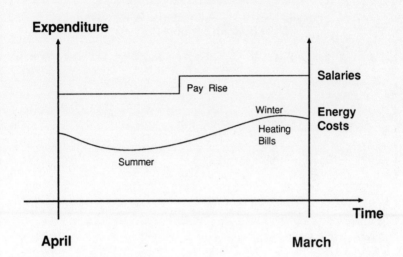

Commitment Accounts

The computerised budgetary control system is of least use on budgets where up-to-date information is required for day-to-day decision making. The problem of the delay in the capture of data relating to payments was discussed in Chapter 2. Discretionary costs are those most affected, and the manager needs some type of 'commitment' accounting system.

A computerised commitment systems would function in the following manner. The manager records his official orders into the computer as they are issued, and the amount is immediately deducted from budget, which then provides an ongoing record of the amount still available to be spent. When the bill for the item is finally received and paid, the charge against the budget is adjusted to reflect any differences between order and invoice price. Successful implementation of a commitment accounting system contains many surprising complications, and few public bodies have an effective system for all of their costs.

In an organisation which does not provide these facilities, the manager would be wise to keep adequate records continuously. An example of such a document is shown in Figure 4.4. There are many variations on this, and the internal auditors may have a standard suggested format that would be suitable for your organisation. Such a record needs to be official and agreed with your deputy; the time when it will be needed most is when you are on holiday or off sick and someone else has to cope with an emergency!

Figure 4.4 Commitment Accounting Sheet Example							
Surgical Ward 15—Non-Sterile Purchases **Initial Budget: £4600—1991–92**							
Date	Order No.	Supplier	Item	Budget Cost £	Actual Cost £	Date Paid	R'm'ng Budget £
15/4/91	105	Regional Supplies	100 Dressing Packs	450	465	28/5	4150
3/5/91	106	Fixit Furniture	Desk & Chair	300	295	6/6	3850
6/5/91	107	Regional Supplies	3 Staff Uniforms	122	122	18/6	3728
22/5/91	108	Medequip	List of Small Items	256			3472
28/5/91		Correction to Order 105		+15			3457
29/5/91	109	Regional Supplies	500 Dressing Packs	240	260	18/6	3217
Month 2 Budget Report				1383	1142		
6/6/91		Correction to Order 106		−5			3222
18/6/91		Correction to Order 109		+20			3202

Notice in Figure 4.4 that whereas actual spending at the end of month 2 (May) is only £465 against a budget of £4,600, the committed expenditure includes order numbers 106, 107 and 109 which were paid in June and order 108 which has not yet been paid. The total committed costs are £1,383, but the high proportion of the budget which is committed is not necessarily a matter for concern. The furniture and the uniforms are almost certainly discretionary items which will not need to be repeated during this year.

For nurse managers in large organisations the section above will provide a basis for keeping adequate budgetary control records. For those charged with running small organisations, there will be the need for more comprehensive records. In the absence of a computerised accounting system, the overall control of the finances depends on the maintenance of an analysed cash book in which all payments and receipts are recorded, but this is outside the scope of this book.

Potential Actions

Budgetary control reporting is of little value if no action is taken to deal with budgets that are out of line. If a budget is overspent or underspent then it is clear that some aspect of your budget plan is not proceeding as expected. The first vital action is to investigate to find the cause. Naturally such investigations should only be in proportion to the problem, but different causes may call for different solutions. For example, it is common for a budget to appear overspent, but only because an inappropriate profile has been applied.

The budget control report is a comparison of actual with estimated spending and highlights differences for investigation. Now, if the problem lies in the plan, and it has been decided that the expenditure is to proceed as before, the three options from Figure 1.2 are available:

(1) **Rethink your original plans**

It is possible that your planning failed to take account of some unexpected development, for example an epidemic, and that the spending has been unavoidable. The correct response may be to present this to the General Manager and request a revision to the plans, and extra finance will need to be found for your budget.

(2) **Revise the Budget**

The budget variance could be caused by a technical error in the original calculation of the budget. Perhaps the wrong pay rates were used, or an inappropriate profile has been applied. A technical correction to the budget may be a feasible response.

(3) **Bid for more resources**

Perhaps the resources devoted to your cost centre assumed a much lower workload than you actually have. There may be a case for returning to the funding body and asking for more. This may certainly be appropriate for a hospital with a block contract negotiated with the DHA.

Budgeting

If the problem is with the actual spending then the suitable actions would be to reduce spending to bring it back into line. But this has a number of variations:

(1) Do nothing—aim for an overspend

- hope that your manager does not notice
- hope that if he notices, he doesn't mind too much because others have underspent to counterbalance
- hope that if he minds, then he cannot or will not take action against you

(2) Cut the spending in the problem area to bring total spending for the year down to budget.

(3) Cut the spending down as far as possible without destroying the service, and hope that the budget is not finally too far over spent.

(4) Exercise your virement powers to switch budget provision from another heading which is underspent to the one that is overspent.

(5) Exercise your virement powers to switch from another heading and then cut back in the other area.

(6) Exercise your carry-forward powers to allow the overspend this year and cut back next year to cover the shortfall.

The availability of virement and carry-forward powers will vary greatly between organisations. Virement is the switching of budget provision from one heading into another. Using the example in Figure 4.1, Judith may wish to transfer £125 out of staffing (which is underspent) into sterile supplies (which is overspent). Carry-forward is the switching of unspent budget from one financial year to the next. Traditionally, public bodies have been very restrictive of both virement and carry-forward powers to maintain tight cash control, but there is some evidence that a more liberal attitude is accompanying recent reforms in public finances.

If you have some flexibility in these areas, you will need to take account of the following series of factors when deciding how to react to a budget overspend:

(1) The controllability of the cost. If no action can be taken by the manager to bring this cost back into line with the budget then other actions need to be considered such as cutting back in more controllable areas. A discretionary budget can usually be cut at short notice by refusing any further purchases.

(2) The sensitivity of the item. Some costs are key to the quality of service, and hence are politically sensitive and cannot be cut without severe consequences. Other costs could be sensitive for other reasons. Senior management will often put heavy constraints

upon the actions that you could take in these cases. However, beware, for you may still be held accountable for an overspend!

(3) The time left in the year for remedial action. An overspend identified early in the year is clearly easier to correct, and the action will need to be less severe. If, for example, you find that wages costs have been overspent by 5% for 9 months of the financial year, it would require a cut of 20% for the remainder of the financial year to restore spending to the budget!

(4) The likely consequence in future years. If the overspending is going to recur next year, then it needs remedial action more urgently than if it is a one-off. Similarly, it is possible to save money by cutting regular maintenance of buildings, but this is not good value in the long term.

(5) The availability of carry-forward and virement powers. Many health authorities will not allow carry forward on any budgets without special dispensation, but virement powers are becoming more common. Virement between budget headings is sometimes permitted only with approval of Finance, but virement between pay and non-pay headings is usually banned because pay, especially nurses' pay, is monitored at higher levels of management as well.

Monitoring Output

The British public sector is still very finance-bound: if spending is in line with the budget then all is well! However, for those concerned with effectiveness, and indeed for those professionals concerned with maximising the service to the public, there is an equal need to monitor throughput, output and outcomes. This subject is developed further in the next chapter, but the concern here is to ensure that information systems which gather financial data are balanced by information systems which report other qualities of the service delivery. The NHS has traditionally gathered a lot of data about throughput, numbers of patients and patient-days, number of prescriptions, number of operations etc., but not so much about quality data, successful interventions, satisfied customers, readmissions etc.

The issue of quality will be addressed further in the next chapter, but the process of budgetary control needs to focus on the extent of the organisation's conformity with the plan both in its financial form and the non-financial. For example, many hospitals now gather regular statistics on readmissions, as one measure of the success of the procedures undertaken. Readmission rates can be estimated and used as a budget and a target by senior management.

For those organisations in a trading situation there is a further requirement in monitoring spending. It would be purposeless to prove that spending was in accordance with the budget if income were inadequate to finance it. In these circumstances it is more important to undertake expenditure/income comparisons rather than expenditure/budget comparisons. In other words, if income is underachieving then spending must be scaled down to that level or the organisation risks liquidation.

Summary

This chapter has provides a review of the issues in controlling a budget. The chapter reminded readers that much of the effort is already in place with the variety of physical controls that are used by public authorities. Furthermore, many organisations will have a comprehensive budget reporting system that informs its managers if a budget is likely to be overspent. However, two areas of potential weaknesses are discussed: firstly, the need for commitment records, especially for discretionary budgets and, secondly, the use of profiles and their suitability. The chapter concludes with a range of hints and suggestions to bear in mind when dealing with an overspent budget.

Exercises and discussion topics

4.1 Discuss the position of Judith Stott.
   (a) How useful is her budget control statement?
   (b) What actions are available to her, and which should she actually take if the current trends continue?

4.2 Consider your budget; to what extent are you bound by physical controls? Do these physical controls prevent you overspending or do you still need to monitor the finances?

4.3 Examine the budgetary control reports that you receive from Finance. Are there any obvious shortcomings that they should correct? Are there shortcomings that require you to keep your own records?

4.4 Review the records that you keep to monitor spending. To what extent are you duplicating centrally held records? To what extent could your records be better designed to provide the information you need?

4.5 To what extent are you monitoring throughput, output or outcomes? Is there an official system for these things, and is its output reported to you for comment?

Chapter 5: Obtaining Value for Money

Case Study

The date is now September 1992, and Judith has been called into a meeting of the management of the hospital. The General Manager is to announce that the hospital is to have a special audit by the Audit Commission looking at the value for money. He has requested this audit to demonstrate the need for more funds for the hospital, and to prove the effectiveness of the hospital.

He is concerned that every manager should be prepared for the auditors, and have a report ready which reviews their unit and demonstrates the good value for money and the high quality of the service. Judith has, of course, always been careful not to be extravagant with public money, but she has never had to defend her spending to external inspectors.

Introduction

The phrase '**Value for Money**' has become a slogan in public sector finance in the last decade. It came to prominence in the early 1980s when public bodies were constantly being accused of waste and extravagance in contrast to private sector where there is a 'profit motive' to stimulate managers to be more efficient and effective! Much of the rhetoric may have been vastly overstated yet it still formed the agenda for a stream of reforms to public services including contracting out, privatisation, and now internal markets. Many informed observers would now probably accept that much of the public service was not organised in a manner designed to make best use of the resources available, and reforms were inevitable. The consequence for public-sector managers (now styled to include many professional groups, not just administrators) is that obtaining value for money is an important part of their duties.

This chapter will look at the issues relating to the evaluation of performance. It will define the concepts of economy, efficiency and effectiveness, it will explore the use of performance indicators and it will examine the scope of judging the performance of a public service.

Performance in the Public Sector

In the private sector, so the theory goes, the firm has to make profits in order to survive. The concept of profit not only provides an immediate measure of success, but also (usually) a stream of cash which will enable the firm to continue to thrive. In the public sector, there is no measure of

51

profit, merely the hand-out of funds to deliver services, and therefore there is no incentive for managers to improve their efficiency, especially when any budget savings achieved will probably only be rewarded by a cut in the budget next year!

The issue has been summarised by Professor Rutherford in a diagram which is reproduced in Figure 5.1. It shows the circular flow of resources in and out of the organisation, and demonstrates that in a budget-financed organisation there is a gap between the outflow of services and the receipt of cash. It is this gap that the internal market is intended to bridge. If the money earned by a hospital depends upon the number of clients then the finance can be regarded as a payment for the service (albeit, from the government rather than the patient) and the organisation turns into a self-sustaining organisation.

This problem was identified many years ago, and in the 1970s there was a drive to find 'output measures' for public services which would give an appropriate basis for judging success; this fizzled out without any major breakthroughs. For many years local authorities and health authorities have produced unit costs for their services; the DoH has gathered and published the 'cost accounts' of DHAs which give costs per patient and costs per inpatient-day. CIPFA statistics have been the vehicle for publishing costs per pupil for the education service, for example, but these documents received little attention outside the accounting profession until the late 1980s.

A more sophisticated analytical tool for analysing public service costs has been developed more recently, called Performance Indicators. These have broadened the concept of the ratio of inputs (costs) to outputs (volume of service), and the DoH now has a package which has been renamed as 'Health Service Indicators' which all DHAs are obliged to produce, and are published as a league table to highlight the most and the least efficient. The book *Taking Action with Indicators* by C Day is a useful guide to this subject.

In other parts of the public sector similar developments have occurred. In the nationalised industries, managers were given performance targets to aim for, and central government departments have been encouraged to develop performance measures which will report upon their success in the delivery of the service. Local Authorities are obliged to reproduce comparative statistics about their performance in their annual reports to enable the electorate to make judgments about the performance. We shall return to the use of performance indicators later in this chapter. But first, let us look at some of the concepts that underpin the use of indicators.

Economy, Efficiency and Effectiveness

The three Es have often been used as the basis for understanding value for money, and the three elements—economy, efficiency, and effectiveness—can be defined using the concepts of the inputs, outputs and

Figure 5.1 Resource Flows in Organizations

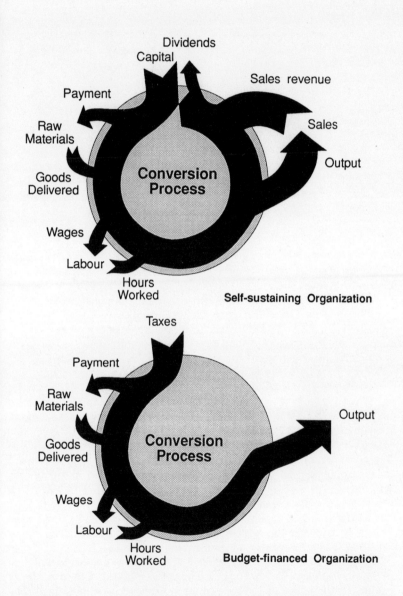

From Rutherford: *Financial Reporting in the Public Sector.* Butterworths.

Figure 5.2 Economy, Efficiency and Effectiveness

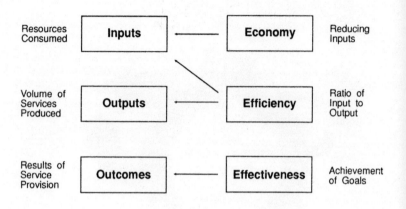

outcomes of the service. Figure 5.2 represents the relationships, which are expanded below:

Economy represents the concept of spending only that money which is available. To economise is to reduce overall spending following a reduction in income. The term also implies a degree of care over spending plans to avoid extravagance and waste. To economise, however, does not imply anything about the volume of output or the level of success of the outcomes; it relates only to the inputs into the service.

The concept of economy is used widely in the review of the purchases of an organisation. For example, the switch to a cheaper supplier for dressings would seem to constitute an improvement in value for money, reducing the inputs. Naturally, there may be an impact on efficiency and effectiveness if the new product is inferior in quality, and takes nurses longer to use. Another example could be the use of thermostats to improve the control of the heating system. In this case an improvement in economy will probably have a beneficial effect on both the efficiency and effectiveness of the organisation.

Efficiency is an engineering term that is used for machines and other processes. It relates the resources input into the process with the output achieved. The efficiency of an electricity power station, for example, can be calculated as the ratio of energy tied up in the coal compared with that of the electricity produced. The efficiency of a pulley is the ratio of energy exerted by the puller on the rope to the work done in lifting a load. The efficiency of a service therefore relates the resources used by that service with the volume of output delivered. Efficiency measures—e.g. cost per patient—are common, and are usually calculated by a ratio:

OUTPUT MEASURE
INPUT MEASURE

There are, of course a range of inputs to each service, and the efficiency of the organisation in utilising those inputs can be measured separately. For example, the efficiency of an outpatients department could be measured using the cost per appointment; but in more detail, the number of staff per 1000 appointments would indicate the efficiency of the use of employees, and the number of appointments per square metre of floor area would measure the utilisation of space.

High figures for these indicators would not necessarily reflect on the outpatient manager. The resources devoted to the outpatients function would have been determined at a higher level of management, and a high level of resources could indicate a higher quality of service to the patient. In addition, a service that is over-resourced could be viewed as a service with excess capacity, whereas a service which is indicated to be highly efficient may simply be over-stretched.

Earlier in the chapter we discussed the ambiguous nature of public services and the difficulty of identifying output measures. As a result, efficiency in any pure sense is difficult to identify; whereas the engineer may be able to define his inputs and outputs precisely in a scientific manner, the outputs in a public service are often complex and contradictory, and in most circumstances a range of indicators is necessary to obtain a balanced picture.

Effectiveness is an even more complex concept to pin down. A service is effective if it achieves the objectives for which it was set up. But the objectives of public services are ambiguous even when stated, and are usually left unstated in British public life. However, objectives can be deduced at times and measures can be devised to indicate the level of success.

One common example in the NHS is the use of waiting lists. It can be assumed that one objective of the NHS is to provide a health service at the time it is needed. The extent to which it is failing to achieve this is measured by the size and length of the waiting list. Many commentators would regard it as blunt and inaccurate, but it is certainly used in that way by politicians.

There would be as many measures of effectiveness for a service as there are concepts of objectives. To an outsider to the health service, for example, it is surprising that there is not more emphasis placed on the success of treatment, perhaps highlighted by readmission rates or perhaps by death/discharge proportions in certain specialties. Naturally, these could not be taken in isolation, but they may reflect more closely the patients' perception of 'success' of the process, in the same way as examination pass rates indicates the academic success of schools.

Budgeting

Cost Effectiveness is a term which links outcomes to inputs, and seeks to analyse the extent to which a change in inputs results in a corresponding change in effectiveness. While recognising the need for effectiveness, it asks whether an increase in effectiveness is worth enough to the organisation to warrant the necessary rise in costs. For example, it could be argued that free dental checks have been relatively effective in maintaining the teeth of the nation, but the government has decided that the cost of the scheme is now so high that it is not cost-effective.

Quality

The subject of performance indicators has been developing in the past few years. The early packages were full of financial calculations which concentrated upon inputs. There is now much more emphasis on 'quality' and customer orientation. The definition of 'quality' is still debated and it must be related to effectiveness (assuming one of the goals of the organisation is to satisfy customers), and in some arenas it has been accepted as 'fitness for purpose'. Public service managers have been challenged by some of the ideas emerging from the book *In Search of Excellence* by Peters and Waterman which advocated, amongst other things, closeness to the client as a key feature of successful businesses. The debate about performance indicators has moved away from simple cost-per-client calculations into concepts of customer satisfaction, and quality of service indicators. For a more detailed examination of this subject, the report published by the National Consumer Council is a useful guide, and many of the ideas are being incorporated into the Citizen's Charter.

Use of Performance Measures

The performance indicators which have been developed throughout the NHS provide information about the economy, efficiency, effectiveness, quality, and other aspects of the service. They generally do not have much meaning on their own. A cost per patient or a length of waiting list carries little significance unless it can be compared with some 'standard', to indicate whether the figure is good or bad and by how much. The choice of standard depends on the circumstances, but there are three basic approaches:

(1) The measure can be prepared in succeeding time periods, and a trend can then be observed. This is commonly used for physical measures such as waiting lists or staff/patient ratios that would be expected to remain relatively static. A movement up or down is then viewed as good or bad depending on the type of measure.

A trend over a longer period of time could be very valuable in observing changes in the service. Figures 5.3a and 5.3b (below)

56

give an example of maternity statistics over a 10-year period showing trends in effectiveness alongside trends in efficiency.

Figure 5.3a Maternity Service Data 1971–1980

	1971	1976	1977	1978	1979	1980
Still-births/1000 total births	12.4	9.6	9.4	8.4	7.9	8.3
Infant (age<1 year) mortality/1000 live births	17.5	14.2	13.7	13.1	12.8	12.0
Neonatal (age <4 weeks) mortality/1000 live births	11.6	9.7	9.2	8.7	8.2	7.6
Perinatal (age <1 week) mortality/1000 total births	22.1	17.6	16.9	15.4	14.6	13.4
Maternal mortality/1000 total births	0.17	0.13	0.13	0.11	0.11	0.11

Figure 5.3b Index of Average Cost per Maternity Inpatient Day 1971/2–1979/80

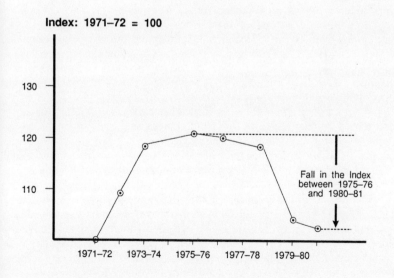

Index: 1971–72 = 100

Fall in the Index between 1975–76 and 1980–81

(2) Comparative statistics provide the opportunity to compare one
unit's performance with that of similar units in other organisations.
Figure 5.4 gives the performance measures for an ambulance
service, encouraging the managers of the worst performing units
to improve. One feature of these statistics is the published 'rank',
that shows where that service is located in the league table of all
ambulance services. The reader must take care to understand
whether Rank 1 of Rank 45 is the better!

(3) The third method of using performance measures is as targets for
managers. Increasingly, senior management are employed on
performance-related pay, and their salaries are dependent on the
achievement of an improvement in certain specified measures.
This trend is likely to continue and may begin to affect middle and
junior managers, especially with the development of competition.
This aspect is specifically promoted in the Citizen's Charter.

*"Targets should be published, together with full and
audited information about the results achieved.
Wherever possible, information should be in
comparable form, so that there is a pressure to emulate
the best".*

This is made more specific in the Government's *Patients' Charter*, which
sets national standards for waiting times for ambulances, in accident and
emergency services, and in outpatients departments. Local standards are to
be established for other waiting times. These are the only measurable
performance indicators to emerge from the document.

Although performance indicators do have much value, their
limitations need to be appreciated. Many of the indicators are easy to
criticise; some are superficial, others can be manipulated, and for others,
differences between hospitals, for example, can be explained by historical
accident rather than management competence. The new Charter right of a
maximum period of two years on the waiting list for treatment has caused
ripples in some health authorities: it has been suggested that some have
overturned clinical priorities to ensure compliance, and that others have
devised schemes to manipulate entry onto the lists, but press reports are
denied by NHS management. Highlighting certain measures may merely
redirect energy towards achieving that particular objective and away from
others of equal worthiness.

The two major criticisms are: firstly, that they concentrate only on the
measurable and provide no information on the unmeasurable aspects of the
service; and secondly, performance indicators often tend to focus on
intermediate objectives only, not on the ultimate aims of the service.
'Output' is often used rather than 'outcome' because it is easier to collect
the data and to quantify. There tend to be relatively few measures that
provide more than a mere glimpse of successful outcomes of the service.

Figure 5.4   Ambulance Services 1981 (Trent Region)

Ambulance Authority	Total Net Cost of Whole Service (£000s)	Whole Service Cost/1000 Population Served (Indicator 20) P1	Rank	Whole Service Cost/1000 Patients Carried (Indicator 21) P1	Rank	Cost of Management & Supervision as % of Total Cost (Indicator 22) P1	Rank	Staff Cost £000s	Staff Nos. WTE	Cost/WTE Ambulance Service Staff (Indicator 23) P1	Rank	Overtime Pay as % of Total Pay (Indicator 24) P1	Rank
S. Yorks. Met.	4,931	3785	41	11,065	14	17.9	10	3744	419.0	8935	13	7.0	30
Derbys.	4,059	4510	27	12,281	5	11.5	39	2972	390.0	7621	39	10.3	21
Leics.	3,305	3953	36	10,988	18	14.7	22	2541	324.2	7838	35	9.1	24
Lincs.	2,888	5367	4	12,524	24	14.4	24	2069	265.6	7792	37	12.2	16
Notts.	5,097	5217	10	12,275	6	19.4	4	3658	418.0	8751	19	4.7	31
Regional Totals	20,280												
Regional Average		4453		11,772		15.6%				8248		8.2%	
England Av.		4572		10,449		14.8				8495		12.2	
England Max.		6266	1	17,385	1	23.8	1			9439	1	18.8	1
England Min.		3284	45	7560	45	10.7	45			7278	45	4.7	31

Rank: This indicates the position of the indicator compared with the 45 Ambulance Authorities of England and Wales

59

Budgeting

To obtain a clear picture of the overall performance of an organisation would require many indicators to be used, and still the unmeasurable aspects will be excluded.

Evaluating Performance

The use of performance measures is inevitably growing, and with more information available to all levels of management, the power to calculate more sophisticated measures is present in most health authorities. The use of the Health Service Indicators appears to be mainly for external reporting and monitoring by supervisory bodies, the RHA and DoH. At that level, the indicators tend to be used as starting points to ask questions and to probe further into a subject. For example, an indicator may show a high cost per cubic metre for heating in a particular hospital. The investigator would then be triggered to examine more closely and ask whether the energy is charged at the correct tariff, whether there is some design problem in the building which implies a large heat loss, whether the thermostat controls are working properly and are set correctly, whether there has been an unusual transaction (e.g. amendment of a previous year's bill) etc.

It can be seen that this type of investigation could be initiated by internal management before any auditors arrive. Indeed, the use of indicators by management is encouraged by the DoH, and is fairly common, especially in the light of the need for efficiency savings in recent years. In fact, it could be argued that the internal use of indicators is likely to be more fruitful; a criticism from outside tends to be met by defensiveness and excuses rather than action.

It has been stressed that the selection of the indicators depend upon goals and values of the reviewer, which may lead to a bias in the review. A management consultant's review would probably focus upon operational efficiency, a medical audit on clinical practices, and a patient may be more interested in convenience and responsiveness of the service. Several writers have recently promoted the concept of 'goal-free evaluation' as a pragmatic, achievable route towards reviewing the effectiveness and performance of a public service. They argue that public services have a wide range of interested parties, each with a valid perspective, each with a different set of 'values'. A goal-free evaluation would seek to discover the concerns of all the stakeholders in a service and attempt to identify from them the relevant 'issues' that should be of concern to managers. By this means managers can make informed decisions about a service without being bound by their own set of 'values'.

One example in the use of goal-free evaluation is in the higher education field. It is common practice for all courses to be reviewed on a regular cycle. This review is undertaken by an external team alongside the course management and calls for the comments of present and past students, lecturing staff, external examiners, institutional management, employers of ex-students, and anyone else that has some 'stake' in the course. In addition the team looks at performance indicators, course recruitment and student progression statistics. The broad range of sources provides a balance to the 'values' of the team itself and enables an authoritative evaluation to take place.

Summary

This chapter examines a series of issues regarding the question of value for money. Many of the exercises below require the calculation of suitable performance indicators followed by a realistic assessment of the value of those calculations. It can be seen that indicators will be used by external parties concerned with reviewing the service, whether they are auditors, management consultants or funding bodies. The selection of the indicators for use will inevitably influence the conclusions of any review, but the emergence of 'quality' indicators as well as financial and throughput measures have broadened the debate, and provide the opportunity for the input of a wide range of views into the process.

Managers who are subject to a review may react in different ways. There has been some tendency towards defensiveness, but in an environment of Total Quality Management, towards which many public bodies are working, there is a recognition that quality—and, by definition, performance—can always be improved. In these circumstances a manager may welcome an external review to assist in the constant search for progress.

The chapter concludes with a discussion of goal-free evaluation and suggests that the import of this concept into the NHS may be a useful adjunct to peer review in the clinical services.

Exercises

5.1 Discuss Judith's situation. Suggest ways in which she can proceed in evaluating her service and preparing for the auditors.

5.2 Identify the performance measures that are calculated by management for your cost centre. Some of these may be out of your control (e.g. bed occupancy rates), but others may be used to evaluate your performance.

5.3 Identify any performance measures for your organisation as a whole that are prominently used (e.g. in its customer-relations publicity material). Are these used fairly? Are there other indicators that are equally valid that may present a different picture?

5.4 A regional manager is considering the over-provision of inpatient facilities for the region for a particular speciality. The Regional Services Accountant has gathered the following information about

Budgeting

two wards in neighbouring hospitals, which could be candidates for closure.

	Northwich DGH	Southwich DGH
Activity Statistics		
Beds Available	30	30
No. of Cases in 1991	300	280
In-patient days in days	6570	7118
Staff Nos. (FTEs)	29	29
Direct Costs		
Nurse Staffing	219,700	219,700
Vacancy Factor	(10,985)	(13,495)
Overtime	0	5215
Uniforms	1385	3480
Medical and Surgical Equipment	15,000	15,200
Drugs	12,000	12,000
	237,100	242,100
Support Costs		
Radiotherapy	6000	5000
Pathology	9000	9000
Catering	9000	9500
Administration	12,000	12,500
Portering	4,500	5000
Works	21,000	20,000
Other Expenses	148,500	143,400
	450,000	448,000

Calculate the health service indicators for these two wards and draft a report to the regional manager on the performance of these two wards. Include in your report an appraisal of the usefulness of this information for his purpose, and discuss any other information that would be more appropriate.

5.5   The Faraway Regional Health Authority has recently published its
Hospital Costs for the year ended 31st March 1981.

From the following extracted information on inpatients you are required to
comment on the costs and statistics of the individual hospitals, indicating
what reservations you may have about such comparisons in the public
sector.

Hospital	A	B	C	D	E
Average available beds	705	688	585	306	177
Average occupied beds	574	564	454	242	128
Number of in-patient days	213845	199149	165616	88330	46595
Number of cases	31294	23142	16993	10711	7985
Expenditure (£000s)	13963	14456	13601	5301	3605

To assist you in this task, you are told that regional averages are:

Occupancy	76%
Average Stay/Case (days)	8.5
Cases/available bed	32.8
Cost/day	£69.08
Cost/case	£583.83

Chapter 6:   Conclusions

Case Study

The date is now March 1993. Judith has prepared her budget for 1993–94 and is now feeling confident in handling her budget. In fact so much so that she has again been offered the opportunity of promotion. Two Assistant Nursing Officer posts are being created in the hospital, one to be responsible for the monitoring of nursing standards and the other to allocate and control the budgets for the wards.

She is trying to decide whether to apply for either, and if so, for which. The General Manager has asked her specifically to apply for the budgeting job; she has the respect of her colleagues and would bring a sensitivity to this challenging post. She herself, however, would prefer the other job and has suggested that an accountant would be better at dealing with budgeting.

Introduction

This final chapter attempts to draw together a number of threads from the book. It briefly considers the nature of budgeting and suggests some useful hints for the nurse promoted to a budget-holding post for the first time.

Budgeting: Technical or Political?

Many years ago finance in the NHS was an issue for the Finance Department. Nobody else understood it and nobody else needed to! Budgeting used to be a subject for the expert; many a nurse manager used to say that the accountant couldn't do the work of the nurse, so why should the nurse do the work of an accountant. It was regarded as a technical skill that was learnt in training, rather like a surgeon learns to perform operations, but this is no longer the case. Budgets are devolved down the hierarchy and managers at all levels are expected to be able to use them.

This does not minimise the technical skill of the accountancy profession. There are concepts to learn and apply, there are techniques to practice, and there is experience to gain which all contribute towards the competence of the accountant. There are certain technical aspects of budget preparation, e.g. the handling of inflation, that have only been touched upon in this book, for which the accountant may be required. When dealing with the organisation as a whole, these problems multiply, and it becomes essential to have a skilled financial manager close to the centre of decision making.

Familiarity and confidence gives the accountant an advantage in budget management. He has the skills, the sources of information and the time (usually) to investigate problems with the budget which make him a useful ally for the nurse manager. However, it does not give him a monopoly; the nurse is the right person to be making resource allocation decisions in a ward, not the accountant.

Budgeting: Inescapable Reality

The second objection that a nurse manager may raise against the subject of this book is that the history of the NHS contains many examples of initiatives in management that have rarely lasted. There is much evidence that changes come in waves, and the situation has never settled before the next wave overtakes the last. Since 1974 the rate of change has steadily picked up pace and the manager could be excused for simply waiting for each wave to blow over!

In this case however, the devolvement of budgets is not a temporary phenomenon. Specialty costs and management budgets may be history but underlying these initiatives was a common thread which is identifiable across the public sector—to break down massive bureaucracies, introduce accountable management down the hierarchy, and to make public servants responsible for their actions. These developments are permanent; they are supported by all political parties and popular with the electorate. As the Citizen's Charter insists:

> *"Services work best where those responsible for providing them can respond directly to the needs of their clients"*

In order to respond directly the nurse manager needs to have control of the finances. The total budget available will always be restricted by public finances, but the deployment of those resources is best determined by local managers dealing directly with their clients.

Budgeting: Resolving the Dilemma

The third objection is that the conflict between professional responsibility and financial accountability is too great. It is not possible, you may say, to feel responsible for the delivery of a standard of care when, as a budget holder, you are also identified with the shortage of funds.

This is a genuine problem for many nurses. Few would enter the nursing profession in order to take responsibility for the cuts in budgets that have fallen on some hospital wards. The selection of a caring career implies a preference for putting people before money. Three arguments will be put forward to counter it.

Firstly, the dilemma which must be faced by nurse managers needs to be faced by somebody. The total resources available will never match the demand, and the cash allocations will always be tight for the service manager; if they were not, how could value for money be assured? The argument in favour of delegated budget management is that the manager at the cost-centre level is in a better position to identify the best uses for the limited resources available. Indeed, the first schools in an experiment in delegated budget management in Cambridgeshire in the mid-1980s tended to find ways of saving money on premises costs and of adding to their staffing.

Secondly, the inputs into the service in the form of cash and manpower are not equal to the outputs or the outcomes. The government is keen to encourage public-sector managers to seek alternative sources of funds, and the nurse manager who can find some will be able to maintain output with falling budgets. Also, in many areas alternative working methods have been found to improve quality while reducing costs. Increasing productivity is normal in the private sector, and the government is expecting it from the public services as well.

The third answer to this objection is not a solution, but a personal strategy for coping with the problem. To the nurse manager with a reduced budget, no external financing available, and no efficiency savings the present may look gloomy and there may be a temptation to try to continue all the previous practices with reduced staffing. But this is a recipe for anxious, guilt-ridden nurses and diminishing productivity and effectiveness. A more realistic approach would be to recognise the reduced resources and plan for them. The nurse manager needs to assess the priorities for action and to plan within the finance available. The job may not be completed as fully as before, but at least the work that is done is given proper attention, and the responsibility for the cuts lies elsewhere.

Learning Jargon or Developing Confidence

But, you may say, dealing with budgets is just common sense; it is like housekeeping. All that is needed is to learn the jargon.

The answer to this question lies throughout this book. It is true that to many the management of a budget is natural; until recent years there was little management training in this area and most managers learned the skills by experience. It is true also that for those who have worked in the private sector, the transition from nurse to manager is often easier, for the changes are largely a result of business language and attitudes being imported into the public sector.

However, the volume of individuals affected by, for example, the introduction of ward budgeting across the country is enormous, and it would be wrong to proceed with these changes without some retraining. Furthermore, there is ample evidence that for many there is a major cultural upheaval to overcome in taking the responsibility for managing a budget. It implies taking a strategic view of the service and trying to obtain the best value for the common good rather than for each individual. It is at this point that the managerial ethic clashes with the professional in the healthcare field, but many have made the transition successfully.

Exercises

6.1 Discuss the position of Judith.

6.2 **Elsware Hospital**

Introduction

This case study presents the scenario of a fictional hospital which is exploring the possibility of developing its ward budgeting processes. Some background information is presented about the hospital and one specific ward in the hospital, and students are invited to discuss their response from four separate situations. The scope for analytical work in the case is limited by the volume of numerical data which is kept to a minimum.

The student is required to assume the role of the ward sister. However, in group discussions it may be valuable for certain members of the group to play other parts to draw the various professional attitudes and values.

Although her official title is 'Ward Sister', this position is increasingly being referred to as 'Ward Manager', and this terminology is sometimes used in this case.

The four situations are:

(1) The Ward Sister is faced with a trend of increasing workload and variable dependency measures throughout the week, leading to evident understaffing at peak times. The problem is how to manage staffing resources in an uncertain environment, subject to a strict budget.

(2) The Unit Accountant has suggested that greater control could be exercised over non-staffing costs if they were under the budgetary control of the ward managers. The Ward Sister is asked for her response to this proposal.

(3) A new consultant is to be appointed to the speciality. The Ward Sister is asked to consider the resources that she will bid for.

(4) The Unit General Manager is proposing to set up clinical directorships. The ward will be affected and the Sister must consider what managerial relationship she would like to see with the Medical Directors.

Background

Elsware Hospital is a medium-sized district general hospital of 620 beds offering a full range of acute services to a population of 160,000. The area is mainly rural in nature and the nearest DGH of comparable size is 30 miles away. Public transport is limited, and the residents are largely dependent on their own transport, although the road network is good.

The management of Elsware Hospital have in recent years been very progressive, looking to be in the forefront of developments in NHS management practice. The management team has a young age profile, but each member is highly experienced and they tend to work together well. The Unit Accountant was amongst the first to produce authoritative speciality cost statements, and use them. For two years the hospital management has been delegating budgets to nursing staff, to allow ward sisters greater flexibility in the deployment of nurses, although this has been subject to the supervision of divisional managers. The management team is in the main enthusiastic about the 1989 White Paper reforms, but is realistic enough to recognise the problems involved in their implementation.

Bunyan Ward is one of 15 wards forming 'A' Division, which covers most of the acute services in the hospital. The Division Manager, Mr D.L. Gate, was recruited to the hospital 2 years ago, and has a very participative style of management with his ward sisters. He is starting to look for his next promotion and needs to demonstrate to his superiors his managerial talents. Bunyan Ward is a single-speciality ward of 15 beds devoted to general surgery. The establishment has been set at 13.5 whole-time equivalent staff, across the range of grades.

The Ward Sister, Ms N. Choir, has been in the post for 3 years and feels that she now has her ward well organised. She is trusted by her divisional manager to look after her own staffing resources, she has a good relationship with the Unit Accountant and Unit Nursing Officer, and she also works well with the consultant who uses her ward. She is ambitious to progress in her career, and is eager to try some of the new ideas in the NHS, so she is keeping up with recent developments.

The full cost of the ward in the calendar year 1989, including all recharged costs, was £303,400. During 1989, 4673 inpatients days were recorded for 702 patients, leading to the following performance indicators compared with the regional average for the speciality:

	Bunyan	**Regional Average**
Cost per case	£432	£429
Cost per inpatient day	£64.93	£68.14
Average occupancy	85.4%	88.7%

Situation One

The staffing of the ward has been a problem for several years. The ideal establishment was agreed three years ago, but although the total numbers of staff are above the establishment, their gradings are rather lower. This reflects the difficulty in recruiting trained nurses in this part of the country and the time lag in training existing staff. Details are shown in the Appendix to this chapter.

The Hospital has a system for recording the dependency measures of each ward on a day-to-day basis. The information is stored in the District Computer, but Mr Gate has obtained a print giving the history of Bunyan Ward for the past 12 months. A summarised version is given below.

Average Dependency Measures for Each Month

1989	Average Dependency (WTE)	1989	Average Dependency (WTE)
Jan	13.6	Jul	13.7
Feb	13.4	Aug	13.8
Mar	13.7	Sep	13.9
Apr	13.9	Oct	13.7
May	13.6	Nov	13.9
Jun	13.8	Dec	14.0

Actual Dependency for Each Day During Two Weeks in January 1990

January 1990	Date	Actual Dep'd'y	Date	Actual Dep'd'y
Sun	8	13.7	15	13.8
Mon	9	13.8	16	14.1
Tue	10	13.8	17	14.5
Wed	11	14.4	18	13.7
Thu	12	14.2	19	14.1
Frid	13	13.7	20	13.9
Sat	14	14.0	21	13.7

Mr Gate has suggested that Ms Choir should review her scheduling of staff times in the light of this information.

   (a) Given the unavailability of extra cash to recruit more staff, identify the options available to the ward manager.

   (b) To what extent can Ms Choir guarantee the quality of care required by the 'nursing standards'?

   (c) To what extent is Ms Choir acting as 'professional' or a 'manager' in the performance of this task?

Situation Two

The 'full cost' of running Bunyan Ward for the financial year 1990/91 has
been calculated by the Unit Accountant as follows:

	£
Nursing Staff	180,820
Nurse Education Recharge	11,200
Catering (supplied from the hospital kitchen)	22,450
Works Department (including power, maintenance etc.)	21,200
Medical and Surgical Equipment	8,700
Drug Costs (including cost of pharmacy)	37,500
Dressings	5,000
Laundry and Linen	10,970
Portering Recharge	4,500
Administration Recharge	11,600
TOTAL	**342,910**

(a) Control of the nursing staff is already delegated to ward sisters at
Elsware Hospital. Examine in turn each of the other above costs,
which represent in some way resources allocated to Bunyan Ward:

   (1) Consider to what extent the ward manager may wish to
influence the level of resource in that area.

   (2) Identify mechanisms (if possible) that would provide the
ward manager with control over these resources.

   (3) Discuss the feasibility and the desirability of using a
financial budget as the main device for the ward manager
to influence resources in this area.

(b) Identify any other aspects of the operation and environment of the
ward which the ward manager may wish to influence that are not
included in the above costs. Evaluate their significance compared
to the financial issues.

Situation 3

Due to the growing demand, the lengthening waiting list, and the consequent pressure on the existing consultant, the Regional Health Authority has decided to appoint a further consultant in General Surgery at Elsware Hospital. He will be using a number of wards, allocating about 20% of his patients to Bunyan. He has been allocated one new theatre session and will be relieving his colleagues in General Surgery at other sessions.

The Unit General Manager (UGM) has approached Mr Gate to identify the extra resources that will be required in Bunyan and other wards, and he in turn has asked Ms Choir for her views. The UGM is normally fair in his allocation of resources, but he has made it clear on several occasions that there is no new money. Any additional costs will have to be met from savings elsewhere, especially from the division seeking extra funds.

Prepare an outline for a bid for resources to be discussed with Mr Gate. You may wish to start by looking at the following areas:

(a) an assessment of the likely number of new patients

(b) the need for extra bed space in the ward

(c) the unavoidable extra costs arising from extra patients

(d) potential savings that could be made within the ward to set against the increased costs

(e) any other action that could be taken to optimise the use of resources in relation to the appointment of the new consultant.

Situation 4

The UGM has proposed that Resource Management should be implemented in Elsware Hospital as soon as possible by the establishment of 'business centres' in the management structure, primarily in the form of clinical directorates. He has not yet fully developed his ideas and is calling a meeting of senior and middle managers to discuss his proposal.

Mr Gate will be invited to the meeting and has asked Ms Choir for her views on the relationship between these new clinical directorates and the wards. He can see two possibilities. The wards could be included in the directorates and would become a resource managed by a 'director', inevitably a senior consultant. Bunyan Ward would come under the control of the Director of General Surgery. Alternatively, the 'A' Division could be established as a business centre in its own right, selling its services to the clinical directors under agreed contracts.

(a) Consider the impact on Bunyan Ward of these alternatives under the following headings:

(i)   The effect on the day-to-day routine of the ward.

(ii) The effect on the positions of Ms Choir and Mr Gate.

(iii) The effectiveness of the Clinical Director to develop his budget.

(iv) The determination of budgets and other resources for the ward.

(v)   The relative power and influence of the medical and nursing professions.

(vi) The quality of service to the patient.

(b) Are there any other models that could be used in the relationship between wards and directorates that have not occurred to Mr Gate?

Appendix

Bunyan Ward Staffing Establishment

Grade	Establishment (W.T.E)	In Post
G	1	1 full time
F	1	0
E	3	2 full time, 1 half-time
D	2	3 full time
C	1.75	2 full time, 2 half-time
A	4.75	4 full time, 1 three-quarter time
Total	13.5	12 full time, 3 half-time, 1 three-quarter time

All staff are scheduled to attempt to provide equal cover each day. Grades D, E, and G staff have been in post for many months and shift patterns are well established.

Further Reading

DAY, C. *Taking Action with Indicators*. London: HMSO, 1989.
This book which has been produced through the DoH gives a readable account of Performance Indicators, as they could be used in the NHS. A interesting feature of the book is the series of case studies which illustrate the utilisation of indicators to analyse and identify solutions to problems.

HENLEY, D., HOLTHAM, C., LIKIERMAN, A. and PERRIN, J. *Public Sector Accounting and Financial Control*. VNR (International), 1989.
Professor Perrin contributed the NHS chapter in this book, but the remainder of the book is also valuable, giving an overview of financial arrangements in other parts of the public sector. In addition, it has general chapters on financial reporting and management accounting across the public services.

NARAYANASAMY, A. *Performance Indicators in Nurse Education & Allied Studies*. Lancaster: Quay Publishing/CHS, 1992.

NATIONAL CONSUMER COUNCIL *Performance Measurement and the Consumer*. NCC, 1987.
This book is the report of a conference in September 1987 organised by the NCC which examined the use of performance measures in local government and the NHS. It was influential in moving the debate away from pure 'accounting' measures towards indicators of customer satisfaction.

PERRIN, J. *Resource Management in the NHS*. VNR, 1988.
Although published before the NHS White Paper of February 1989 this book provides an excellent exposition of NHS financial and resource management. Professor Perrin has a long-standing involvement with the NHS dating back to the Royal Commission in the 1970s, and gives a historical perspective to the developments in the NHS in the past few years.

TAYLOR, I. and POPHAM, P. *An Introduction to Public Sector Management*. Unwin, 1989.
This book provides the same type of overview across the public sector as HENLEY *et al.*, but in the field of management. Again usefully, there are some general chapters early in the book one of which is titled 'Financial Management'.

Glossary of Abbreviations

CIPFA	Chartered Institute of Public Finance and Accountancy
DGH	District General Hospital
DGM	District General Manager
DHA	District Health Authority
DoH	Department of Health
DSS	Department of Social Security
FHSA	Family Health Services Association
FTE	Full-Time Equivalent
GP	General Practitioner
NHS	National Health Service
NHT	National Health Service Trust
PESC	Public Expenditure Survey Committee
PEWP	Public Expenditure White Paper
RAWP	Resource Allocation Working Party
RHA	Regional Health Authority
UGM	Unit General Manager
VAT	Value Added Tax
VFM	Value for Money
WRVS	Women's Royal Voluntary Services Association
WTE	Whole-Time Equivalent

Index

O

Opportunity costs, 19
Original estimate, 4
Output monitoring, 49
Overheads, 10
Overspends
  Dealing with, 47

P

Patient costing, 11
Performance evaluation, 51, 58
Performance indicators, 52
Performance measures, 56, 58–60
Profiles, 44
Public Expenditure Survey, 6
Public Expenditure White Paper, 6

Q

Quality, 56

R

Regional Health Authority, 5
Resource allocation, 27

Resource reviews, 31
Revenue budget, 2
Revenue costs, 10

S

Speciality costs, 10
Stepped costs, 17

T

Top-down budgeting, 25
Total Quality Management, 61

V

Value for money, 51
Variable costs, 16
VAT, 15
Virement, 5, 48

W

Workload estimation, 30

Z

Zero-base bidding, 27